Mademoiselle

Set In Soul

© 2022 Tatiana Media LLC in partnership with Set In Soul LLC

ISBN #: 978-1-949874-10-5

Published by Tatiana Media LLC

For general information on our other products and services, please contact our Customer Support within the United States at support@setinsoul.com.

Tatiana Media LLC as well as Set In Soul LLC publishes its books in a variety of electronic formats. Some content that appears in print may not be available in electronic books.

THIS JOURNAL BELONGS TO

Dedicated To My Future Wonderful Self. Get To Know Me Now.

Table Of Contents

How To Use This Journal

Growing up it can be hard to say the things that we feel yet be so easy to be misunderstood. There are times where certain things can feel way too big to even give them a name. This is why learning how to communicate our thoughts and feelings (even if it's just through the written word) helps us to get our points across and allows us to have a better chance of being understood. You are always being taught to use your words and journaling is one of the best places to do just that.

Journaling can help us to really learn the many amazing things about ourselves such as what makes us react to things, being aware of what we like, and so on. It gives us a sense of awareness that is our own instead of something that someone else pointed out to us. Although other people's feedback has its use in its own way (especially when it comes to our parents), our inherent knowledge and discoveries, the things that feel true to us and would resonate with us will always come from within. Writing about these thoughts and instances would help us to foster confidence regarding our inner compass and help us make the right choices in our lives.

We recommend taking the time out to write in this journal every morning and every night. Always take your time when filling out the journal prompts. There is no pressure to have the right answer because there is no right answer. This journal will serve as your most quiet but yet most expressive best friend. Have fun with it. This is your real life unfolding and you get to tell the story. Over time you will look back at what you have written and see how much you have evolved with certain situations and how your life has blossomed. You are living in an amazing world where you can create anything. You are the princess in your story and it's time you learned more about yourself and start creating your dream story in every area of your life. This is your chance to be heard. Now Mademoiselle, let's get started.

My Firsts

What Are My Firsts?

About Me

About Me

I Am:

I Am From:

I Love:

My Favorite Animal:

My Favorite Movie:

About Me

My Favorite Color:

My Favorite Food:

My Favorite Book:

My Favorite Song:

My Favorite Season:

About Me

My Favorite Thing To Do:

My Favorite Holiday:

I Would Describe Myself:

I Look:

I Am:

About Me

I Want To Travel To:

What Do I Dream About?

I Like To Sing:

Do I Believe I Am A 'Good' Person?

If I Responded No To The Previous Prompt, Then Why Do I Believe That I Am Not A 'Good' Person?

About Me

I Really Like:

I Do Not Like:

I Like To Spend Time:

I Want To Learn:

I Know How To:

About Me

I Am Excited About:

I Am Nervous About:

I Am Good At:

I Like To Give:

I Like To Help:

About Me

It Is Hard For Me:

What Do I Worry About?

Who Do I Believe Loves Me?

Great Things That Have Happened To Me:

I Like To Share:

About Me

It Feels Good To:

I Wonder:

What Do I Want To Change?

I Feel Alone:

I Feel Left Out When:

About Me

Some Days I Feel:

I Have Not Told Anyone:

I Saw And Never Told Anyone:

Based On My Response To The Previous Prompt, How Did What I See
Make Me Feel And When Will I Tell Someone?

I Think It Is Cool To:

About Me

I Like To Read:

I Want To Know:

It Hurts My Feelings:

I Am Sorry For:

I Want To Buy:

About Me

I Wish I Could:

On The Weekends I Like To:

I Am Confused About:

I Feel Uncomfortable When:

I Like Spending Time With:

About Me

I Want To Try:

The First Thing I Do When I Wake Up:

The First Thing That I Do When I Wake Up:

Right Before I Go To Sleep, I Like To:

I Like Talking About:

About Me

I Do Not Like It When People Ask:

The Oldest Thing That I Remember:

I Am Done With:

I Wish I Had More Time To:

I Am Afraid Of:

About Me

What Is Important To Me?

The Best Thing About Being A Girl:

What Makes Me Happy?

Who Do I Make Happy?

I Did Not Do:

About Me

When Someone Says Something Nice To Me:

When Someone Says Something Mean To Me:

Am I A Good Listener?

What Makes Me Laugh?

Do I Believe I Am Pretty?

About Me

If I Responded No To The Previous Prompt, Why Do I Believe I Am Not Pretty?

Do I Believe I Am Smart?

If I Responded No To The Previous Prompt, Why Do I Believe I Am Not Smart?

I Know A Lot About:

I Wish People:

About Me

Next Year I Will:

For My Next Birthday:

When I Am Alone, I Think About:

I Get Sad About:

Based On My Response To The Previous Prompt, Why Do I Get Sad About That?

About Me

I Keep Asking For:

I Want People To Hear Me:

I Think Boys Are:

I Think Girls Are:

I Want:

About Me

I Recently Experienced:

I Have Fun:

I Feel Protected When:

Do I Love Myself?

Do I Respect Myself?

About Me

Do I Respect Others?

What Do I Want To Do Better With?

I Look Up To:

I Get To Choose:

When People Do Not Like Me, I:

About Me

I Try To Fit In By:

It Is Okay If I Am Not Like Everyone Else Because:

Last Year Was Different From This Year:

I Need Help With:

I Want To Start:

About Me

I Sometimes Cry About:

I Am Interested In:

I Am Not Scared To:

I Help Other Girls:

Extra Notes

My Body

Talk

My Body Talk

My Body Is:

Is My Body Changing?

If I Responded Yes To The Previous Prompt, In What Ways Is My Body Changing?

Have I Gotten Taller?

Do I Wear Braces Or Any Form Of Teeth/Mouth Correctors?

My Body Talk

If I Responded Yes To The Previous Prompt, How Does Wearing Braces Or Any Form Of Teeth/Mouth Correctors Make Me Feel?

Do I Have Acne, Blemishes, And/Or Dark Spots?

If I Responded Yes To The Previous Prompt, How Does Having Acne, Blemishes, And/Or Dark Spots Makes Me Feel And How Am I Treating It?

Do I Wear Glasses?

If I Responded Yes To The Previous Prompt, How Do I Feel When I Wear My Glasses?

My Body Talk

What Else About Me Is Growing?

What Is My Current Clothing Size?

What Is My Current Shoe Size?

Am I Currently Wearing A Bra?

If I Responded Yes To The Previous Prompt, What Is My Current Bra Size?

My Body Talk

Have I Gotten My Period For The First Time Yet?

If I Responded Yes To The Previous Prompt, When Did I Get My Period And How Did It Feel To Get My Period For The First Time?

I Am Amazing Because:

I Am Beautiful Because:

I Want:

My Body Talk

I Want To Feel:

I Love Being Me Because:

What Do I Like About My Hair?

What Do I Like About My Skin?

When I Pick Out Clothes For Myself, I Look For:

Extra Notes

God

God

I Believe God:

I Know God Is:

I Trust God To:

I Like To Tell God:

I Like To Ask God:

God

When I Pray To God, I Say:

The Last Prayer God Answered:

God Is:

God Helps Me:

Extra Notes

My Home Life

My Home Life

My Parents Are:

My Parents Are From:

I Currently Live With:

Who Do I Consider Part Of My Family?

What Does My Family Do Together?

My Home Life

I Like Spending Time With:

At Home I Feel:

Do I Feel Safe At Home?

If I Responded No To The Previous Prompt, Why Do I Feel This Way?

What Am I Afraid To Tell My Parents/Caretakers?

My Home Life

I Like It When My Mom/Caretaker (Complete If Applicable):

I Like It When My Dad/Caretaker (Complete If Applicable):

I Asked My Mom/Dad/Caretaker:

I Got Blamed For:

I Have Gotten In Trouble For (Complete If Applicable):

My Home Life

What Have I Learned From Getting In Trouble (Complete If Applicable)?

I Want To Tell My Mom/Dad/Caretaker:

What Do I Like About My Family (Answer If Applicable)?

What Do I Not Like About My Family (Answer If Applicable)?

When I Am At Home, I Have To:

My Home Life

What Do I Do On The Weekends?

It Is Fun To:

At Home, I Am Called:

What Do I Like To Do At Home?

When I Am Home, I Look Forward To:

Extra Notes

My Crushes And More

My Crushes And More

Do I Have A Crush On Anybody?

If I Responded Yes To The Previous Prompt, Who Do I Have A Crush On?

Do I Feel Different When I Am Around My Crush?

Do I Try To Make My Crush Like Me?

Is It Okay If My Crush Does Not Like Me?

My Crushes And More

Can I Be Friends With My Crush?

Who Do I Talk To About My Crush?

Do I Feel Embarrassed Talking About My Crush?

Does My Crush Make Me Smile?

Does Anyone Have A Crush On Me?

My Crushes And More

If I Responded Yes To The Previous Prompt, Who Has A Crush On Me And How Do I Know?

What Does It Mean To Have A Crush On Someone?

What Makes Me Like Someone?

How Does It Feel To Have A Crush?

I Feel Loved When:

My Crushes And More

What Do I Do When Someone Says They Like Me?

Extra Notes

My Friends

My Friends

My Friends Are:

Who Is My Best Friend?

What Do I Like About My Friends?

What Do My Friends And I Have In Common?

Who Use To Be My Friend?

My Friends

Based On My Response To The Previous Prompt, Why Are We No Longer Friends?

Do I Consider Myself To Be 'Friendly?'

Do I Believe I Am A 'Good' Friend?

Are My Friends Nice To Me?

Who Do I Want To Be Friends With?

My Friends

Based On My Response To The Previous Prompt, Why Do I Want To Be Friends With This Person?

Who Wants To Be Friends With Me?

Based On My Response To The Previous Prompt, Why Do They Want To Be Friends With Me?

Have My Friends Ever Made Fun Of Me?

If I Responded Yes To The Previous Prompt, Why Did They Make Fun Of Me?

My Friends

Have I Ever Made Fun Of Any Of My Friends?

If I Responded Yes To The Previous Prompt, Which Of My Friends Have I Made Fun Of And Why Did I Make Fun Of Them?

What Games Do My Friends And I Play?

What Do My Friends And I Like To Do?

What Makes Me Stop Becoming Someone's Friend?

My Friends

My Friends Are My Friends Because:

Extra Notes

School

School

What School Do I Go To?

What Grade Am I In?

Who Is/Are My Teacher/s?

My Teacher/s:

My School Counselor:

School

School Is:

I Like School Because (Complete If Applicable):

I Do Not Like School Because (Complete If Applicable):

My Favorite Thing To Do In School:

My Favorite Subject To Learn:

School

My Least Favorite Subject In School Is:

Based On My Response To The Previous Prompt, Why Is This My Least Favorite Subject In School?

In School, I Am Known As:

I Always Look Forward To:

How Well Am I Doing In School?

School

Has Anyone (Outside Of My Friends) Made Fun Of Me?

If I Responded Yes To The Previous Prompt, Who Made Fun Of Me?

Based On My Response To The Previous Prompt, Why Did They Make Fun Of Me?

Have I Ever Made Fun Of Anyone (Outside Of My Friends)?

If I Responded Yes To The Previous Prompt, Who Did I Make Fun Of?

School

Based On My Response To The Previous Prompt, Why Did I Make Fun Of This Person?

In School, I Am Learning:

What School Events Are Fun?

What Activities Am I A Part Of In School?

What Would Make School Better?

Extra Notes

When I Get Older

When I Get Older

I Want To Grow Up To Be:

I Am Going To Be A Girl Who:

What Does My Future Look Like In One Year?

What Does My Future Look Like In Five Years?

What Does My Future Look Like In Ten Years?

When I Get Older

How Will I Help My Family?

How Will I Help My Community?

How Will I Change The World?

I Look Forward To:

I Will Be Successful At:

Extra Notes

A Girl's

World

A Girl's World

Date: Mood:

Morning Thoughts

I Am Grateful For:

I Am Excited About:

Today I Am Asking God For:

Today I Want To Know:

Today's Compliment To Myself:

What Would I Like To Express?

Nightly Thoughts

What Happened Today?

Today I Tried My Best To:

What Did I Like About My Day?

Someone Told Me:

Today I Thought About:

I Am Proud Of Myself For:

Tonight's Self-Talk:

A Girl's World

Date: Mood:

Morning Thoughts

I Am Grateful For: I Am Excited About:

Today I Am Asking God For: Today I Want To Know:

Today's Compliment To Myself: What Would I Like To Express?

Nightly Thoughts

What Happened Today?   Today I Tried My Best To:

What Did I Like About My Day?   Someone Told Me:

Today I Thought About:

I Am Proud Of Myself For: Tonight's Self-Talk:

A Girl's World

Date: Mood:

Morning Thoughts

I Am Grateful For: I Am Excited About:

Today I Am Asking God For: Today I Want To Know:

Today's Compliment To Myself: What Would I Like To Express?

Nightly Thoughts

What Happened Today?   Today I Tried My Best To:

What Did I Like About My Day?   Someone Told Me:

Today I Thought About:

I Am Proud Of Myself For: Tonight's Self-Talk:

Happy Looks Good On Me.

A Girl's World

Date: Mood:

Morning Thoughts

I Am Grateful For:

Today I Am Asking God For:

Today's Compliment To Myself:

I Am Excited About:

Today I Want To Know:

What Would I Like To Express?

Nightly Thoughts

What Happened Today?

What Did I Like About My Day?

Today I Thought About:

I Am Proud Of Myself For:

Today I Tried My Best To:

Someone Told Me:

Tonight's Self-Talk:

A Girl's World

Date: Mood:

Morning Thoughts

I Am Grateful For:

I Am Excited About:

Today I Am Asking God For:

Today I Want To Know:

Today's Compliment To Myself:

What Would I Like To Express?

Nightly Thoughts

What Happened Today?

Today I Tried My Best To:

What Did I Like About My Day?

Someone Told Me:

Today I Thought About:

I Am Proud Of Myself For:

Tonight's Self-Talk:

A Girl's World

Date: Mood:

Morning Thoughts

I Am Grateful For: I Am Excited About:

Today I Am Asking God For: Today I Want To Know:

Today's Compliment To Myself: What Would I Like To Express?

Nightly Thoughts

What Happened Today?   Today I Tried My Best To:

What Did I Like About My Day?   Someone Told Me:

Today I Thought About:

I Am Proud Of Myself For: Tonight's Self-Talk:

My Dreams Can Come True.

God
Watches
Over Me.

A Girl's World

Date: Mood:

Morning Thoughts

I Am Grateful For: I Am Excited About:

Today I Am Asking God For: Today I Want To Know:

Today's Compliment To Myself: What Would I Like To Express?

Nightly Thoughts

What Happened Today?   Today I Tried My Best To:

What Did I Like About My Day?   Someone Told Me:

Today I Thought About:

I Am Proud Of Myself For: Tonight's Self-Talk:

A Girl's World

Date: Mood:

Morning Thoughts

I Am Grateful For: I Am Excited About:

Today I Am Asking God For: Today I Want To Know:

Today's Compliment To Myself: What Would I Like To Express?

Nightly Thoughts

What Happened Today?   Today I Tried My Best To:

What Did I Like About My Day?   Someone Told Me:

Today I Thought About:

I Am Proud Of Myself For: Tonight's Self-Talk:

A Girl's World

Date: Mood:

Morning Thoughts

I Am Grateful For: I Am Excited About:

Today I Am Asking God For: Today I Want To Know:

Today's Compliment To Myself: What Would I Like To Express?

Nightly Thoughts

What Happened Today?   Today I Tried My Best To:

What Did I Like About My Day?   Someone Told Me:

Today I Thought About:

I Am Proud Of Myself For: Tonight's Self-Talk:

A Girl's World

Date: Mood:

Morning Thoughts

I Am Grateful For: I Am Excited About:

Today I Am Asking God For: Today I Want To Know:

Today's Compliment To Myself: What Would I Like To Express?

Nightly Thoughts

What Happened Today?   Today I Tried My Best To:

What Did I Like About My Day?   Someone Told Me:

Today I Thought About:

I Am Proud Of Myself For: Tonight's Self-Talk:

I Believe In....

Wherever I Go, I Will Shine.

A Girl's World

Date: Mood:

Morning Thoughts

I Am Grateful For: I Am Excited About:

Today I Am Asking God For: Today I Want To Know:

Today's Compliment To Myself: What Would I Like To Express?

Nightly Thoughts

What Happened Today?   Today I Tried My Best To:

What Did I Like About My Day?   Someone Told Me:

Today I Thought About:

I Am Proud Of Myself For: Tonight's Self-Talk:

A Girl's World

Date: Mood:

Morning Thoughts

I Am Grateful For: I Am Excited About:

Today I Am Asking God For: Today I Want To Know:

Today's Compliment To Myself: What Would I Like To Express?

Nightly Thoughts

What Happened Today?   Today I Tried My Best To:

What Did I Like About My Day?   Someone Told Me:

Today I Thought About:

I Am Proud Of Myself For: Tonight's Self-Talk:

A Girl's World

Date: Mood:

Morning Thoughts

I Am Grateful For:

Today I Am Asking God For:

Today's Compliment To Myself:

I Am Excited About:

Today I Want To Know:

What Would I Like To Express?

Nightly Thoughts

What Happened Today?

What Did I Like About My Day?

Today I Thought About:

I Am Proud Of Myself For:

Today I Tried My Best To:

Someone Told Me:

Tonight's Self-Talk:

A Girl's World

Date: Mood:

Morning Thoughts

I Am Grateful For: I Am Excited About:

Today I Am Asking God For: Today I Want To Know:

Today's Compliment To Myself: What Would I Like To Express?

Nightly Thoughts

What Happened Today?   Today I Tried My Best To:

What Did I Like About My Day?   Someone Told Me:

Today I Thought About:

I Am Proud Of Myself For: Tonight's Self-Talk:

I Love Expressing Myself.

A Girl's World

Date: _____   Mood: _____

Morning Thoughts

I Am Grateful For: I Am Excited About:

Today I Am Asking God For: Today I Want To Know:

Today's Compliment To Myself: What Would I Like To Express?

Nightly Thoughts

What Happened Today?   Today I Tried My Best To:

What Did I Like About My Day?   Someone Told Me:

Today I Thought About:

I Am Proud Of Myself For: Tonight's Self-Talk:

A Girl's World

Date: Mood:

Morning Thoughts

I Am Grateful For: I Am Excited About:

Today I Am Asking God For: Today I Want To Know:

Today's Compliment To Myself: What Would I Like To Express?

Nightly Thoughts

What Happened Today?   Today I Tried My Best To:

What Did I Like About My Day?   Someone Told Me:

Today I Thought About:

I Am Proud Of Myself For: Tonight's Self-Talk:

A Girl's World

Date: Mood:

Morning Thoughts

I Am Grateful For:

I Am Excited About:

Today I Am Asking God For:

Today I Want To Know:

Today's Compliment To Myself:

What Would I Like To Express?

Nightly Thoughts

What Happened Today?

Today I Tried My Best To:

What Did I Like About My Day?

Someone Told Me:

Today I Thought About:

I Am Proud Of Myself For:

Tonight's Self-Talk:

I like

Standing

Out.

A Girl's World

Date: Mood:

Morning Thoughts

I Am Grateful For: I Am Excited About:

Today I Am Asking God For: Today I Want To Know:

Today's Compliment To Myself: What Would I Like To Express?

Nightly Thoughts

What Happened Today?   Today I Tried My Best To:

What Did I Like About My Day?   Someone Told Me:

Today I Thought About:

I Am Proud Of Myself For: Tonight's Self-Talk:

A Girl's World

Date: Mood:

Morning Thoughts

I Am Grateful For: I Am Excited About:

Today I Am Asking God For: Today I Want To Know:

Today's Compliment To Myself: What Would I Like To Express?

Nightly Thoughts

What Happened Today?   Today I Tried My Best To:

What Did I Like About My Day?   Someone Told Me:

Today I Thought About:

I Am Proud Of Myself For: Tonight's Self-Talk:

A Girl's World

Date: Mood:

Morning Thoughts

I Am Grateful For:

I Am Excited About:

Today I Am Asking God For:

Today I Want To Know:

Today's Compliment To Myself:

What Would I Like To Express?

Nightly Thoughts

What Happened Today?

Today I Tried My Best To:

What Did I Like About My Day?

Someone Told Me:

Today I Thought About:

I Am Proud Of Myself For:

Tonight's Self-Talk:

A Girl's World

Date: Mood:

Morning Thoughts

I Am Grateful For:

Today I Am Asking God For:

Today's Compliment To Myself:

I Am Excited About:

Today I Want To Know:

What Would I Like To Express?

Nightly Thoughts

What Happened Today?

What Did I Like About My Day?

Today I Thought About:

I Am Proud Of Myself For:

Today I Tried My Best To:

Someone Told Me:

Tonight's Self-Talk:

I Am Pretty And
I Am Amazing.
I Guess That
Makes Me
Pretty Amazing.

A Girl's World

Date: Mood:

Morning Thoughts

I Am Grateful For: I Am Excited About:

Today I Am Asking God For: Today I Want To Know:

Today's Compliment To Myself: What Would I Like To Express?

Nightly Thoughts

What Happened Today?   Today I Tried My Best To:

What Did I Like About My Day?   Someone Told Me:

Today I Thought About:

I Am Proud Of Myself For: Tonight's Self-Talk:

A Girl's World

Date: Mood:

Morning Thoughts

I Am Grateful For: I Am Excited About:

Today I Am Asking God For: Today I Want To Know:

Today's Compliment To Myself: What Would I Like To Express?

Nightly Thoughts

What Happened Today?   Today I Tried My Best To:

What Did I Like About My Day?   Someone Told Me:

Today I Thought About:

I Am Proud Of Myself For: Tonight's Self-Talk:

A Girl's World

Date: Mood:

Morning Thoughts

I Am Grateful For:

Today I Am Asking God For:

Today's Compliment To Myself:

I Am Excited About:

Today I Want To Know:

What Would I Like To Express?

Nightly Thoughts

What Happened Today?

What Did I Like About My Day?

Today I Thought About:

I Am Proud Of Myself For:

Today I Tried My Best To:

Someone Told Me:

Tonight's Self-Talk:

A Girl's World

Date: Mood:

Morning Thoughts

I Am Grateful For:

I Am Excited About:

Today I Am Asking God For:

Today I Want To Know:

Today's Compliment To Myself:

What Would I Like To Express?

Nightly Thoughts

What Happened Today?

Today I Tried My Best To:

What Did I Like About My Day?

Someone Told Me:

Today I Thought About:

I Am Proud Of Myself For:

Tonight's Self-Talk:

The Princess

1 - beige   2 - pink   3 - purple   4 - brown   5 - yellow

6 - orange   7 - red   8 - light brown   9 - liliac

A Girl's World

Date: Mood:

Morning Thoughts

I Am Grateful For: I Am Excited About:

Today I Am Asking God For: Today I Want To Know:

Today's Compliment To Myself: What Would I Like To Express?

Nightly Thoughts

What Happened Today?   Today I Tried My Best To:

What Did I Like About My Day?   Someone Told Me:

Today I Thought About:

I Am Proud Of Myself For: Tonight's Self-Talk:

A Girl's World

Date: Mood:

Morning Thoughts

I Am Grateful For: I Am Excited About:

Today I Am Asking God For: Today I Want To Know:

Today's Compliment To Myself: What Would I Like To Express?

Nightly Thoughts

What Happened Today?   Today I Tried My Best To:

What Did I Like About My Day?   Someone Told Me:

Today I Thought About:

I Am Proud Of Myself For: Tonight's Self-Talk:

A Girl's World

Date: Mood:

Morning Thoughts

I Am Grateful For:

Today I Am Asking God For:

Today's Compliment To Myself:

I Am Excited About:

Today I Want To Know:

What Would I Like To Express?

Nightly Thoughts

What Happened Today?

What Did I Like About My Day?

Today I Thought About:

I Am Proud Of Myself For:

Today I Tried My Best To:

Someone Told Me:

Tonight's Self-Talk:

I Am Doing So Well.

A Girl's World

Date: Mood:

Morning Thoughts

I Am Grateful For:

I Am Excited About:

Today I Am Asking God For:

Today I Want To Know:

Today's Compliment To Myself:

What Would I Like To Express?

Nightly Thoughts

What Happened Today?

Today I Tried My Best To:

What Did I Like About My Day?

Someone Told Me:

Today I Thought About:

I Am Proud Of Myself For:

Tonight's Self-Talk:

A Girl's World

Date: Mood:

Morning Thoughts

I Am Grateful For: I Am Excited About:

Today I Am Asking God For: Today I Want To Know:

Today's Compliment To Myself: What Would I Like To Express?

Nightly Thoughts

What Happened Today?   Today I Tried My Best To:

What Did I Like About My Day?   Someone Told Me:

Today I Thought About:

I Am Proud Of Myself For: Tonight's Self-Talk:

A Girl's World

Date: Mood:

Morning Thoughts

I Am Grateful For: I Am Excited About:

Today I Am Asking God For: Today I Want To Know:

Today's Compliment To Myself: What Would I Like To Express?

Nightly Thoughts

What Happened Today?   Today I Tried My Best To:

What Did I Like About My Day?   Someone Told Me:

Today I Thought About:

I Am Proud Of Myself For: Tonight's Self-Talk:

A Girl's World

Date: _____   Mood: _____

Morning Thoughts

I Am Grateful For:

I Am Excited About:

Today I Am Asking God For:

Today I Want To Know:

Today's Compliment To Myself:

What Would I Like To Express?

Nightly Thoughts

What Happened Today?

Today I Tried My Best To:

What Did I Like About My Day?

Someone Told Me:

Today I Thought About:

I Am Proud Of Myself For:

Tonight's Self-Talk:

A Girl's World

Date: Mood:

Morning Thoughts

I Am Grateful For: I Am Excited About:

Today I Am Asking God For: Today I Want To Know:

Today's Compliment To Myself: What Would I Like To Express?

Nightly Thoughts

What Happened Today?   Today I Tried My Best To:

What Did I Like About My Day?   Someone Told Me:

Today I Thought About:

I Am Proud Of Myself For: Tonight's Self-Talk:

I Am A Great Friend.

No Is A Powerful Word.

A Girl's World

Date: Mood:

Morning Thoughts

I Am Grateful For: I Am Excited About:

Today I Am Asking God For: Today I Want To Know:

Today's Compliment To Myself: What Would I Like To Express?

Nightly Thoughts

What Happened Today?   Today I Tried My Best To:

What Did I Like About My Day?   Someone Told Me:

Today I Thought About:

I Am Proud Of Myself For: Tonight's Self-Talk:

A Girl's World

Date: _____   Mood: _____

Morning Thoughts

I Am Grateful For:

Today I Am Asking God For:

Today's Compliment To Myself:

I Am Excited About:

Today I Want To Know:

What Would I Like To Express?

Nightly Thoughts

What Happened Today?

What Did I Like About My Day?

Today I Thought About:

I Am Proud Of Myself For:

Today I Tried My Best To:

Someone Told Me:

Tonight's Self-Talk:

A Girl's World

Date: Mood:

Morning Thoughts

I Am Grateful For: I Am Excited About:

Today I Am Asking God For: Today I Want To Know:

Today's Compliment To Myself: What Would I Like To Express?

Nightly Thoughts

What Happened Today?   Today I Tried My Best To:

What Did I Like About My Day? Someone Told Me:

Today I Thought About:

I Am Proud Of Myself For: Tonight's Self-Talk:

A Girl's World

Date: Mood:

Morning Thoughts

I Am Grateful For: I Am Excited About:

Today I Am Asking God For: Today I Want To Know:

Today's Compliment To Myself: What Would I Like To Express?

Nightly Thoughts

What Happened Today?   Today I Tried My Best To:

What Did I Like About My Day?   Someone Told Me:

Today I Thought About:

I Am Proud Of Myself For: Tonight's Self-Talk:

I Am Comfortable In My Own Skin.

I Am Inspired By....

A Girl's World

Date: Mood:

Morning Thoughts

I Am Grateful For: I Am Excited About:

Today I Am Asking God For: Today I Want To Know:

Today's Compliment To Myself: What Would I Like To Express?

Nightly Thoughts

What Happened Today?   Today I Tried My Best To:

What Did I Like About My Day?   Someone Told Me:

Today I Thought About:

I Am Proud Of Myself For: Tonight's Self-Talk:

A Girl's World

Date: Mood:

Morning Thoughts

I Am Grateful For:

I Am Excited About:

Today I Am Asking God For:

Today I Want To Know:

Today's Compliment To Myself:

What Would I Like To Express?

Nightly Thoughts

What Happened Today?

Today I Tried My Best To:

What Did I Like About My Day?

Someone Told Me:

Today I Thought About:

I Am Proud Of Myself For:

Tonight's Self-Talk:

A Girl's World

Date: Mood:

Morning Thoughts

I Am Grateful For: I Am Excited About:

Today I Am Asking God For: Today I Want To Know:

Today's Compliment To Myself: What Would I Like To Express?

Nightly Thoughts

What Happened Today?   Today I Tried My Best To:

What Did I Like About My Day?   Someone Told Me:

Today I Thought About:

I Am Proud Of Myself For: Tonight's Self-Talk:

A Girl's World

Date: Mood:

Morning Thoughts

I Am Grateful For:

I Am Excited About:

Today I Am Asking God For:

Today I Want To Know:

Today's Compliment To Myself:

What Would I Like To Express?

Nightly Thoughts

What Happened Today?

Today I Tried My Best To:

What Did I Like About My Day?

Someone Told Me:

Today I Thought About:

I Am Proud Of Myself For:

Tonight's Self-Talk:

A Girl's World

Date: _____   Mood: _____

Morning Thoughts

I Am Grateful For:

I Am Excited About:

Today I Am Asking God For:

Today I Want To Know:

Today's Compliment To Myself:

What Would I Like To Express?

Nightly Thoughts

What Happened Today?

Today I Tried My Best To:

What Did I Like About My Day?

Someone Told Me:

Today I Thought About:

I Am Proud Of Myself For:

Tonight's Self-Talk:

A Girl's World

Date: Mood:

Morning Thoughts

I Am Grateful For: I Am Excited About:

Today I Am Asking God For: Today I Want To Know:

Today's Compliment To Myself: What Would I Like To Express?

Nightly Thoughts

What Happened Today?   Today I Tried My Best To:

What Did I Like About My Day?   Someone Told Me:

Today I Thought About:

I Am Proud Of Myself For: Tonight's Self-Talk:

A Girl's World

Date: Mood:

Morning Thoughts

I Am Grateful For: I Am Excited About:

Today I Am Asking God For: Today I Want To Know:

Today's Compliment To Myself: What Would I Like To Express?

Nightly Thoughts

What Happened Today?   Today I Tried My Best To:

What Did I Like About My Day?   Someone Told Me:

Today I Thought About:

I Am Proud Of Myself For: Tonight's Self-Talk:

A Girl's World

Date: Mood:

Morning Thoughts

I Am Grateful For: I Am Excited About:

Today I Am Asking God For: Today I Want To Know:

Today's Compliment To Myself: What Would I Like To Express?

Nightly Thoughts

What Happened Today?   Today I Tried My Best To:

What Did I Like About My Day?   Someone Told Me:

Today I Thought About:

I Am Proud Of Myself For: Tonight's Self-Talk:

A Girl's World

Date: Mood:

Morning Thoughts

I Am Grateful For: I Am Excited About:

Today I Am Asking God For: Today I Want To Know:

Today's Compliment To Myself: What Would I Like To Express?

Nightly Thoughts

What Happened Today?   Today I Tried My Best To:

What Did I Like About My Day?   Someone Told Me:

Today I Thought About:

I Am Proud Of Myself For: Tonight's Self-Talk:

A Girl's World

Date: _____   Mood: _____

Morning Thoughts

I Am Grateful For:

Today I Am Asking God For:

Today's Compliment To Myself:

I Am Excited About:

Today I Want To Know:

What Would I Like To Express?

Nightly Thoughts

What Happened Today?

What Did I Like About My Day?

Today I Thought About:

I Am Proud Of Myself For:

Today I Tried My Best To:

Someone Told Me:

Tonight's Self-Talk:

I Am Loved For Who I Am.

What Do I Pray About?

A Girl's World

Date: Mood:

Morning Thoughts

I Am Grateful For: I Am Excited About:

Today I Am Asking God For: Today I Want To Know:

Today's Compliment To Myself: What Would I Like To Express?

Nightly Thoughts

What Happened Today?   Today I Tried My Best To:

What Did I Like About My Day?   Someone Told Me:

Today I Thought About:

I Am Proud Of Myself For: Tonight's Self-Talk:

A Girl's World

Date: Mood:

Morning Thoughts

I Am Grateful For: I Am Excited About:

Today I Am Asking God For: Today I Want To Know:

Today's Compliment To Myself: What Would I Like To Express?

Nightly Thoughts

What Happened Today?   Today I Tried My Best To:

What Did I Like About My Day?   Someone Told Me:

Today I Thought About:

I Am Proud Of Myself For: Tonight's Self-Talk:

A Girl's World

Date: _____   Mood: _____

Morning Thoughts

I Am Grateful For: I Am Excited About:

Today I Am Asking God For: Today I Want To Know:

Today's Compliment To Myself: What Would I Like To Express?

Nightly Thoughts

What Happened Today?   Today I Tried My Best To:

What Did I Like About My Day?   Someone Told Me:

Today I Thought About:

I Am Proud Of Myself For: Tonight's Self-Talk:

Stay

True To

Yourself.

If I Put My
Mind To It
And Believe,
Then I Know I
Can Do It

A Girl's World

Date: Mood:

Morning Thoughts

I Am Grateful For: I Am Excited About:

Today I Am Asking God For: Today I Want To Know:

Today's Compliment To Myself: What Would I Like To Express?

Nightly Thoughts

What Happened Today?   Today I Tried My Best To:

What Did I Like About My Day?   Someone Told Me:

Today I Thought About:

I Am Proud Of Myself For: Tonight's Self-Talk:

A Girl's World

Date: Mood:

Morning Thoughts

I Am Grateful For:

I Am Excited About:

Today I Am Asking God For:

Today I Want To Know:

Today's Compliment To Myself:

What Would I Like To Express?

Nightly Thoughts

What Happened Today?

Today I Tried My Best To:

What Did I Like About My Day?

Someone Told Me:

Today I Thought About:

I Am Proud Of Myself For:

Tonight's Self-Talk:

A Girl's World

Date: Mood:

Morning Thoughts

I Am Grateful For: I Am Excited About:

Today I Am Asking God For: Today I Want To Know:

Today's Compliment To Myself: What Would I Like To Express?

Nightly Thoughts

What Happened Today?   Today I Tried My Best To:

What Did I Like About My Day?   Someone Told Me:

Today I Thought About:

I Am Proud Of Myself For: Tonight's Self-Talk:

A Girl's World

Date: Mood:

Morning Thoughts

I Am Grateful For: I Am Excited About:

Today I Am Asking God For: Today I Want To Know:

Today's Compliment To Myself: What Would I Like To Express?

Nightly Thoughts

What Happened Today?   Today I Tried My Best To:

What Did I Like About My Day?   Someone Told Me:

Today I Thought About:

I Am Proud Of Myself For: Tonight's Self-Talk:

I Feel

```
P  H  W  N  A  P  Q  O  L  C  S  H  K  W  K  P  V  C
B  B  U  N  O  E  Q  V  O  J  I  R  S  N  Y  Z  W  W
B  B  N  N  W  I  I  P  V  G  X  A  T  N  H  Z  D  E
D  E  P  N  Q  A  B  C  A  G  R  Q  H  Y  W  E  O  U
I  N  Z  J  O  H  C  P  B  E  T  L  X  I  T  H  P  C
W  A  R  N  K  T  J  C  L  J  G  A  Y  A  H  V  F  B
K  T  R  D  S  G  N  Y  E  L  W  O  V  A  W  B  S  T
V  Q  P  U  G  G  I  E  A  P  Z  I  W  E  T  J  P  A
T  Y  S  B  E  R  E  X  W  I  T  C  O  F  R  W  T  N
H  O  G  C  R  G  L  U  D  O  K  E  N  N  C  T  B  U
O  W  V  U  B  D  A  Y  M  N  C  R  D  S  T  L  E  B
R  H  H  L  X  F  T  C  M  J  N  N  E  X  X  U  D  B
E  U  O  N  J  T  V  C  R  J  H  A  R  E  L  Y  M  Z
Q  C  T  F  E  U  H  E  P  M  J  M  F  H  O  G  C  T
Y  P  N  R  Y  X  R  R  V  F  Q  C  U  Q  E  X  B  K
A  N  P  H  V  B  Y  H  X  Q  Z  A  L  Z  J  U  D  D
E  H  G  V  K  N  C  Z  K  X  Z  E  E  O  K  P  I  B
G  B  Y  H  S  Z  I  Q  I  Y  Q  S  L  K  M  Z  L  X
```

Accepted   Pretty

Lovable   Wonderful

Motivated

Completed Word Search Can Be Found On Page 327

148

I Am Intelligent

A Girl's World

Date: Mood:

Morning Thoughts

I Am Grateful For: I Am Excited About:

Today I Am Asking God For: Today I Want To Know:

Today's Compliment To Myself: What Would I Like To Express?

Nightly Thoughts

What Happened Today?   Today I Tried My Best To:

What Did I Like About My Day?   Someone Told Me:

Today I Thought About:

I Am Proud Of Myself For: Tonight's Self-Talk:

A Girl's World

Date: Mood:

Morning Thoughts

I Am Grateful For:

I Am Excited About:

Today I Am Asking God For:

Today I Want To Know:

Today's Compliment To Myself:

What Would I Like To Express?

Nightly Thoughts

What Happened Today?

Today I Tried My Best To:

What Did I Like About My Day?

Someone Told Me:

Today I Thought About:

I Am Proud Of Myself For:

Tonight's Self-Talk:

A Girl's World

Date: Mood:

Morning Thoughts

I Am Grateful For: I Am Excited About:

Today I Am Asking God For: Today I Want To Know:

Today's Compliment To Myself: What Would I Like To Express?

Nightly Thoughts

What Happened Today?   Today I Tried My Best To:

What Did I Like About My Day?   Someone Told Me:

Today I Thought About:

I Am Proud Of Myself For: Tonight's Self-Talk:

My

Ideas Are

Great.

A Girl's World

Date: Mood:

Morning Thoughts

I Am Grateful For: I Am Excited About:

Today I Am Asking God For: Today I Want To Know:

Today's Compliment To Myself: What Would I Like To Express?

Nightly Thoughts

What Happened Today?   Today I Tried My Best To:

What Did I Like About My Day?   Someone Told Me:

Today I Thought About:

I Am Proud Of Myself For: Tonight's Self-Talk:

A Girl's World

Date: Mood:

Morning Thoughts

I Am Grateful For: I Am Excited About:

Today I Am Asking God For: Today I Want To Know:

Today's Compliment To Myself: What Would I Like To Express?

Nightly Thoughts

What Happened Today?   Today I Tried My Best To:

What Did I Like About My Day?   Someone Told Me:

Today I Thought About:

I Am Proud Of Myself For: Tonight's Self-Talk:

A Girl's World

Date: Mood:

Morning Thoughts

I Am Grateful For: I Am Excited About:

Today I Am Asking God For: Today I Want To Know:

Today's Compliment To Myself: What Would I Like To Express?

Nightly Thoughts

What Happened Today?   Today I Tried My Best To:

What Did I Like About My Day?   Someone Told Me:

Today I Thought About:

I Am Proud Of Myself For: Tonight's Self-Talk:

I Do Not Want To Look Like Everyone Else. I Love Looking Like Me.

My Attitude Makes A Difference.

A Girl's World

Date: Mood:

Morning Thoughts

I Am Grateful For:

I Am Excited About:

Today I Am Asking God For:

Today I Want To Know:

Today's Compliment To Myself:

What Would I Like To Express?

Nightly Thoughts

What Happened Today?

Today I Tried My Best To:

What Did I Like About My Day?

Someone Told Me:

Today I Thought About:

I Am Proud Of Myself For:

Tonight's Self-Talk:

A Girl's World

Date: Mood:

Morning Thoughts

I Am Grateful For: I Am Excited About:

Today I Am Asking God For: Today I Want To Know:

Today's Compliment To Myself: What Would I Like To Express?

Nightly Thoughts

What Happened Today?   Today I Tried My Best To:

What Did I Like About My Day?   Someone Told Me:

Today I Thought About:

I Am Proud Of Myself For: Tonight's Self-Talk:

Beautiful Unicorn

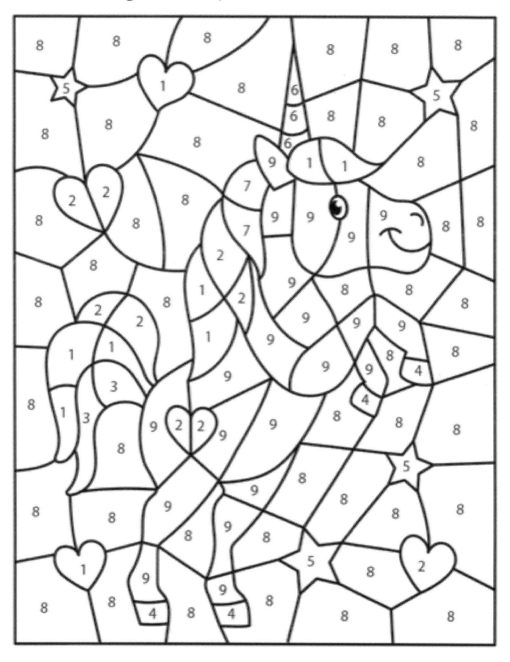

1 - pink   2 - red   3 - green   4 - purple   5 - yellow

6 - orange   7 - light green   8 - light blue   9 - liliac

A Girl's World

Date: _____   Mood: _____

Morning Thoughts

I Am Grateful For:

I Am Excited About:

Today I Am Asking God For:

Today I Want To Know:

Today's Compliment To Myself:

What Would I Like To Express?

Nightly Thoughts

What Happened Today?

Today I Tried My Best To:

What Did I Like About My Day?

Someone Told Me:

Today I Thought About:

I Am Proud Of Myself For:

Tonight's Self-Talk:

A Girl's World

Date: Mood:

Morning Thoughts

I Am Grateful For: I Am Excited About:

Today I Am Asking God For: Today I Want To Know:

Today's Compliment To Myself: What Would I Like To Express?

Nightly Thoughts

What Happened Today?   Today I Tried My Best To:

What Did I Like About My Day?   Someone Told Me:

Today I Thought About:

I Am Proud Of Myself For: Tonight's Self-Talk:

A Girl's World

Date: Mood:

Morning Thoughts

I Am Grateful For: I Am Excited About:

Today I Am Asking God For: Today I Want To Know:

Today's Compliment To Myself: What Would I Like To Express?

Nightly Thoughts

What Happened Today?   Today I Tried My Best To:

What Did I Like About My Day?   Someone Told Me:

Today I Thought About:

I Am Proud Of Myself For: Tonight's Self-Talk:

How Have I Changed Since Last Year?

A Girl's World

Date: Mood:

Morning Thoughts

I Am Grateful For: I Am Excited About:

Today I Am Asking God For: Today I Want To Know:

Today's Compliment To Myself: What Would I Like To Express?

Nightly Thoughts

What Happened Today?   Today I Tried My Best To:

What Did I Like About My Day?   Someone Told Me:

Today I Thought About:

I Am Proud Of Myself For: Tonight's Self-Talk:

A Girl's World

Date: Mood:

Morning Thoughts

I Am Grateful For:

Today I Am Asking God For:

Today's Compliment To Myself:

I Am Excited About:

Today I Want To Know:

What Would I Like To Express?

Nightly Thoughts

What Happened Today?

What Did I Like About My Day?

Today I Thought About:

I Am Proud Of Myself For:

Today I Tried My Best To:

Someone Told Me:

Tonight's Self-Talk:

A Girl's World

Date: Mood:

Morning Thoughts

I Am Grateful For: I Am Excited About:

Today I Am Asking God For: Today I Want To Know:

Today's Compliment To Myself: What Would I Like To Express?

Nightly Thoughts

What Happened Today?   Today I Tried My Best To:

What Did I Like About My Day?   Someone Told Me:

Today I Thought About:

I Am Proud Of Myself For: Tonight's Self-Talk:

It Is Okay If I Change My Mind.

Nature

```
Z W T O Y S U N S E T S Q W B F H O
K E L O Y U T Z U C T L L X U R T W
T Z X R L N B A N E Z P F F T X K L
G J H Z A R P O R S M I H R T P D V
A W C F A I R F R S Y U F A E F E W
I T B J Q S N N B D Y B E E R H Q Q
T M K I Z E T B D A X T G O F L N T
O I N P A O Q F O C E A N S L M H Y
S E D V M Y A H A W S Q X F I D F S
E Q M O U N T A I N S K Z Q E Q E M
V R R Q B D H X F L O W E R S A B A
Y W B G I O D N A B Y L H M V V L O
C I H C A Q A M V G K G W L S W E C
G W C J B C I L M D D O K J E V F R
S V S T E N Y Y G B L B D W Q P F P
D K O Z A J F Z X V Y X B P L C P B
E S X E C K E H Q A X A H P N N J V
F U G G H I M V U Y Z B E L A Z O V
```

Animals   Oceans

Beach   Rainbows

Butterflies   Stars

Flowers   Sunrise

Mountains   Sunsets

Completed Word Search Can Be Found On Page 328

A Girl's World

Date: Mood:

Morning Thoughts

I Am Grateful For: I Am Excited About:

Today I Am Asking God For: Today I Want To Know:

Today's Compliment To Myself: What Would I Like To Express?

Nightly Thoughts

What Happened Today?   Today I Tried My Best To:

What Did I Like About My Day?   Someone Told Me:

Today I Thought About:

I Am Proud Of Myself For: Tonight's Self-Talk:

A Girl's World

Date: Mood:

Morning Thoughts

I Am Grateful For: I Am Excited About:

Today I Am Asking God For: Today I Want To Know:

Today's Compliment To Myself: What Would I Like To Express?

Nightly Thoughts

What Happened Today?   Today I Tried My Best To:

What Did I Like About My Day?   Someone Told Me:

Today I Thought About:

I Am Proud Of Myself For: Tonight's Self-Talk:

A Girl's World

Date: Mood:

Morning Thoughts

I Am Grateful For: I Am Excited About:

Today I Am Asking God For: Today I Want To Know:

Today's Compliment To Myself: What Would I Like To Express?

Nightly Thoughts

What Happened Today?   Today I Tried My Best To:

What Did I Like About My Day?   Someone Told Me:

Today I Thought About:

I Am Proud Of Myself For: Tonight's Self-Talk:

Telling The Truth Feels Good.

I Choose To Be Happy.

A Girl's World

Date: Mood:

Morning Thoughts

I Am Grateful For:

Today I Am Asking God For:

Today's Compliment To Myself:

I Am Excited About:

Today I Want To Know:

What Would I Like To Express?

Nightly Thoughts

What Happened Today?

What Did I Like About My Day?

Today I Thought About:

I Am Proud Of Myself For:

Today I Tried My Best To:

Someone Told Me:

Tonight's Self-Talk:

A Girl's World

Date: Mood:

Morning Thoughts

I Am Grateful For: I Am Excited About:

Today I Am Asking God For: Today I Want To Know:

Today's Compliment To Myself: What Would I Like To Express?

Nightly Thoughts

What Happened Today?   Today I Tried My Best To:

What Did I Like About My Day?   Someone Told Me:

Today I Thought About:

I Am Proud Of Myself For: Tonight's Self-Talk:

Great Happy Friend

1 - light blue   2 - liliac   3 - beige   4 - purple   5 - yellow

6 - red   7 - light green   8 - pink   9 - blue

A Girl's World

Date: Mood:

Morning Thoughts

I Am Grateful For: I Am Excited About:

Today I Am Asking God For: Today I Want To Know:

Today's Compliment To Myself: What Would I Like To Express?

Nightly Thoughts

What Happened Today?   Today I Tried My Best To:

What Did I Like About My Day?   Someone Told Me:

Today I Thought About:

I Am Proud Of Myself For: Tonight's Self-Talk:

A Girl's World

Date: Mood:

Morning Thoughts

I Am Grateful For: I Am Excited About:

Today I Am Asking God For: Today I Want To Know:

Today's Compliment To Myself: What Would I Like To Express?

Nightly Thoughts

What Happened Today?   Today I Tried My Best To:

What Did I Like About My Day?   Someone Told Me:

Today I Thought About:

I Am Proud Of Myself For: Tonight's Self-Talk:

A Girl's World

Date: Mood:

Morning Thoughts

I Am Grateful For: I Am Excited About:

Today I Am Asking God For: Today I Want To Know:

Today's Compliment To Myself: What Would I Like To Express?

Nightly Thoughts

What Happened Today?   Today I Tried My Best To:

What Did I Like About My Day?   Someone Told Me:

Today I Thought About:

I Am Proud Of Myself For: Tonight's Self-Talk:

A Girl's World

Date: Mood:

Morning Thoughts

I Am Grateful For: I Am Excited About:

Today I Am Asking God For: Today I Want To Know:

Today's Compliment To Myself: What Would I Like To Express?

Nightly Thoughts

What Happened Today?   Today I Tried My Best To:

What Did I Like About My Day?   Someone Told Me:

Today I Thought About:

I Am Proud Of Myself For: Tonight's Self-Talk:

If I Could Do Anything Right Now, It Would Be....

I Can Do It.

I Can Do It.

I Can Do It.

A Girl's World

Date: Mood:

Morning Thoughts

I Am Grateful For: I Am Excited About:

Today I Am Asking God For: Today I Want To Know:

Today's Compliment To Myself: What Would I Like To Express?

Nightly Thoughts

What Happened Today?   Today I Tried My Best To:

What Did I Like About My Day?   Someone Told Me:

Today I Thought About:

I Am Proud Of Myself For: Tonight's Self-Talk:

A Girl's World

Date: Mood:

Morning Thoughts

I Am Grateful For: I Am Excited About:

Today I Am Asking God For: Today I Want To Know:

Today's Compliment To Myself: What Would I Like To Express?

Nightly Thoughts

What Happened Today?   Today I Tried My Best To:

What Did I Like About My Day?   Someone Told Me:

Today I Thought About:

I Am Proud Of Myself For: Tonight's Self-Talk:

A Girl's World

Date: Mood:

Morning Thoughts

I Am Grateful For: I Am Excited About:

Today I Am Asking God For: Today I Want To Know:

Today's Compliment To Myself: What Would I Like To Express?

Nightly Thoughts

What Happened Today?   Today I Tried My Best To:

What Did I Like About My Day?   Someone Told Me:

Today I Thought About:

I Am Proud Of Myself For: Tonight's Self-Talk:

A Girl's World

Date: Mood:

Morning Thoughts

I Am Grateful For: I Am Excited About:

Today I Am Asking God For: Today I Want To Know:

Today's Compliment To Myself: What Would I Like To Express?

Nightly Thoughts

What Happened Today?   Today I Tried My Best To:

What Did I Like About My Day?   Someone Told Me:

Today I Thought About:

I Am Proud Of Myself For: Tonight's Self-Talk:

A Girl's World

Date: Mood:

Morning Thoughts

I Am Grateful For:

Today I Am Asking God For:

Today's Compliment To Myself:

I Am Excited About:

Today I Want To Know:

What Would I Like To Express?

Nightly Thoughts

What Happened Today?

What Did I Like About My Day?

Today I Thought About:

I Am Proud Of Myself For:

Today I Tried My Best To:

Someone Told Me:

Tonight's Self-Talk:

A Girl's World

Date: Mood:

Morning Thoughts

I Am Grateful For: I Am Excited About:

Today I Am Asking God For: Today I Want To Know:

Today's Compliment To Myself: What Would I Like To Express?

Nightly Thoughts

What Happened Today?   Today I Tried My Best To:

What Did I Like About My Day?   Someone Told Me:

Today I Thought About:

I Am Proud Of Myself For: Tonight's Self-Talk:

I Am Oh So Worthy Of All The Great And Wonderful Things Just As I Am.

I Can Be Anything I Want To Be.

A Girl's World

Date: Mood:

Morning Thoughts

I Am Grateful For: I Am Excited About:

Today I Am Asking God For: Today I Want To Know:

Today's Compliment To Myself: What Would I Like To Express?

Nightly Thoughts

What Happened Today?   Today I Tried My Best To:

What Did I Like About My Day?   Someone Told Me:

Today I Thought About:

I Am Proud Of Myself For: Tonight's Self-Talk:

A Girl's World

Date: Mood:

Morning Thoughts

I Am Grateful For: I Am Excited About:

Today I Am Asking God For: Today I Want To Know:

Today's Compliment To Myself: What Would I Like To Express?

Nightly Thoughts

What Happened Today?   Today I Tried My Best To:

What Did I Like About My Day?   Someone Told Me:

Today I Thought About:

I Am Proud Of Myself For: Tonight's Self-Talk:

A Girl's World

Date: Mood:

Morning Thoughts

I Am Grateful For: I Am Excited About:

Today I Am Asking God For: Today I Want To Know:

Today's Compliment To Myself: What Would I Like To Express?

Nightly Thoughts

What Happened Today?   Today I Tried My Best To:

What Did I Like About My Day?   Someone Told Me:

Today I Thought About:

I Am Proud Of Myself For: Tonight's Self-Talk:

Random Fun Things To Do

```
G  A  T  P  K  W  A  L  Q  N  D  E  I  X  A  R  C  H
A  K  L  S  P  U  B  P  W  D  P  L  Y  S  F  Q  S  E
B  M  O  L  M  O  C  O  T  G  R  Q  R  Z  U  O  W  C
G  Y  T  F  T  O  C  C  L  Z  O  E  U  A  K  Z  R  H
N  L  D  V  O  D  R  O  U  L  V  H  A  X  Y  I  E  B
V  H  T  I  S  H  W  N  O  O  N  L  M  M  B  O  W  S
O  R  O  C  Z  C  O  V  P  K  R  S  I  Z  I  P  D  I
X  V  Q  C  V  M  Z  E  S  R  I  Q  Z  Z  Q  N  X  R
J  M  O  U  C  X  E  R  Q  I  V  N  J  B  N  D  G  O
K  J  D  E  O  L  S  S  Q  P  V  Z  G  W  D  S  J  T
V  A  X  C  S  Z  H  A  M  Q  A  J  W  R  A  K  U  A
K  H  N  U  S  U  O  T  R  A  V  E  L  I  N  G  Z  V
D  G  H  W  V  C  P  I  H  B  N  M  V  T  C  K  J  C
P  L  T  J  O  S  P  O  R  T  S  W  C  I  I  F  N  Z
I  D  E  A  C  T  I  N  G  J  C  B  G  N  N  Y  J  X
R  T  Q  G  E  K  N  S  J  Y  V  K  O  G  G  J  R  I
R  C  B  J  F  D  G  S  Y  T  H  N  R  X  X  Z  M  F
X  B  M  K  V  U  N  E  E  N  E  J  D  K  Z  L  V  R
```

Acting

Conversations

Cooking

Dancing

Dreaming

Shopping

Sleepovers

Sports

Traveling

Writing

Completed Word Search Can Be Found On Page 329

A Girl's World

Date: Mood:

Morning Thoughts

I Am Grateful For: I Am Excited About:

Today I Am Asking God For: Today I Want To Know:

Today's Compliment To Myself: What Would I Like To Express?

Nightly Thoughts

What Happened Today?   Today I Tried My Best To:

What Did I Like About My Day?   Someone Told Me:

Today I Thought About:

I Am Proud Of Myself For: Tonight's Self-Talk:

A Girl's World

Date: Mood:

Morning Thoughts

I Am Grateful For: I Am Excited About:

Today I Am Asking God For: Today I Want To Know:

Today's Compliment To Myself: What Would I Like To Express?

Nightly Thoughts

What Happened Today?   Today I Tried My Best To:

What Did I Like About My Day?   Someone Told Me:

Today I Thought About:

I Am Proud Of Myself For: Tonight's Self-Talk:

Accept And Love Your Body.

A Girl's World

Date: Mood:

Morning Thoughts

I Am Grateful For: I Am Excited About:

Today I Am Asking God For: Today I Want To Know:

Today's Compliment To Myself: What Would I Like To Express?

Nightly Thoughts

What Happened Today?   Today I Tried My Best To:

What Did I Like About My Day?   Someone Told Me:

Today I Thought About:

I Am Proud Of Myself For: Tonight's Self-Talk:

A Girl's World

Date: Mood:

Morning Thoughts

I Am Grateful For: I Am Excited About:

Today I Am Asking God For: Today I Want To Know:

Today's Compliment To Myself: What Would I Like To Express?

Nightly Thoughts

What Happened Today?   Today I Tried My Best To:

What Did I Like About My Day?   Someone Told Me:

Today I Thought About:

I Am Proud Of Myself For: Tonight's Self-Talk:

A Girl's World

Date: Mood:

Morning Thoughts

I Am Grateful For:

I Am Excited About:

Today I Am Asking God For:

Today I Want To Know:

Today's Compliment To Myself:

What Would I Like To Express?

Nightly Thoughts

What Happened Today?

Today I Tried My Best To:

What Did I Like About My Day?

Someone Told Me:

Today I Thought About:

I Am Proud Of Myself For:

Tonight's Self-Talk:

God Is

```
Q U Q R K O U U Y D K I Q S M T G M
R Y K E H V R U C F X J P K B F G G
L Y L E X E R D T L P Q A L C V Q B
G N T X K C L N V W H I T W K O B F
B K H A O H T C O V Z V I R S R E I
A J M E R C I F U L I H E H D N M R
I D Z K E P H R U L E R N Q I H O I
X N K F K K O R O B I T T E Z I T C
L R R S W I S E V T Q M P U R E O G
Y E O D V O N K H N S S I E O H H D
P D S A U Y N G R N J V P T E U U Y
I E S V F O I D Z O S U G S L G S P
Y E A T T L J J E S S F N Z S E R K
G M C Y R B J A C R O B X R W P S Y
D E R J O O K Z Z M F O B O T B P S
H R E V D H N V I R T U O U S E C G
X P D H M P O G Q R H O L Y Q I Y C
D L G J Q C A S F V E J H I K U T X
```

Holy

King

Light

Limitless

Maker

Merciful

Patient

Perfect

Pure

Redeemer

Ruler

Sacred

Savior

Strong

Superior

Virtuous

Virtuous

Wise

Wonderful

Completed Word Search Can Be Found On Page 330

My Five Favorite Songs Are....

1.

2.

3.

4.

5.

A Girl's World

Date: Mood:

Morning Thoughts

I Am Grateful For: I Am Excited About:

Today I Am Asking God For: Today I Want To Know:

Today's Compliment To Myself: What Would I Like To Express?

Nightly Thoughts

What Happened Today?   Today I Tried My Best To:

What Did I Like About My Day?   Someone Told Me:

Today I Thought About:

I Am Proud Of Myself For: Tonight's Self-Talk:

A Girl's World

Date: _____   Mood: _____

Morning Thoughts

I Am Grateful For:

Today I Am Asking God For:

Today's Compliment To Myself:

I Am Excited About:

Today I Want To Know:

What Would I Like To Express?

Nightly Thoughts

What Happened Today?

What Did I Like About My Day?

Today I Thought About:

I Am Proud Of Myself For:

Today I Tried My Best To:

Someone Told Me:

Tonight's Self-Talk:

A Girl's World

Date: Mood:

Morning Thoughts

I Am Grateful For: I Am Excited About:

Today I Am Asking God For: Today I Want To Know:

Today's Compliment To Myself: What Would I Like To Express?

Nightly Thoughts

What Happened Today?   Today I Tried My Best To:

What Did I Like About My Day?   Someone Told Me:

Today I Thought About:

I Am Proud Of Myself For: Tonight's Self-Talk:

A Girl's World

Date: Mood:

Morning Thoughts

I Am Grateful For: I Am Excited About:

Today I Am Asking God For: Today I Want To Know:

Today's Compliment To Myself: What Would I Like To Express?

Nightly Thoughts

What Happened Today?   Today I Tried My Best To:

What Did I Like About My Day?   Someone Told Me:

Today I Thought About:

I Am Proud Of Myself For: Tonight's Self-Talk:

I Will Not Allow Anyone To Make Me Feel Bad.

A Girl's World

Date: Mood:

Morning Thoughts

I Am Grateful For: I Am Excited About:

Today I Am Asking God For: Today I Want To Know:

Today's Compliment To Myself: What Would I Like To Express?

Nightly Thoughts

What Happened Today?   Today I Tried My Best To:

What Did I Like About My Day?   Someone Told Me:

Today I Thought About:

I Am Proud Of Myself For: Tonight's Self-Talk:

A Girl's World

Date: Mood:

Morning Thoughts

I Am Grateful For: I Am Excited About:

Today I Am Asking God For: Today I Want To Know:

Today's Compliment To Myself: What Would I Like To Express?

Nightly Thoughts

What Happened Today?   Today I Tried My Best To:

What Did I Like About My Day?   Someone Told Me:

Today I Thought About:

I Am Proud Of Myself For: Tonight's Self-Talk:

A Girl's World

Date: Mood:

Morning Thoughts

I Am Grateful For: I Am Excited About:

Today I Am Asking God For: Today I Want To Know:

Today's Compliment To Myself: What Would I Like To Express?

Nightly Thoughts

What Happened Today?   Today I Tried My Best To:

What Did I Like About My Day?   Someone Told Me:

Today I Thought About:

I Am Proud Of Myself For: Tonight's Self-Talk:

A Great Compliment Someone Ever Gave Me....

I Belong To God. God Loves Me.

A Girl's World

Date: _____   Mood: _____

Morning Thoughts

I Am Grateful For:

Today I Am Asking God For:

Today's Compliment To Myself:

I Am Excited About:

Today I Want To Know:

What Would I Like To Express?

Nightly Thoughts

What Happened Today?

What Did I Like About My Day?

Today I Thought About:

I Am Proud Of Myself For:

Today I Tried My Best To:

Someone Told Me:

Tonight's Self-Talk:

A Girl's World

Date: Mood:

Morning Thoughts

I Am Grateful For: I Am Excited About:

Today I Am Asking God For: Today I Want To Know:

Today's Compliment To Myself: What Would I Like To Express?

Nightly Thoughts

What Happened Today?   Today I Tried My Best To:

What Did I Like About My Day?   Someone Told Me:

Today I Thought About:

I Am Proud Of Myself For: Tonight's Self-Talk:

A Girl's World

Date: Mood:

Morning Thoughts

I Am Grateful For: I Am Excited About:

Today I Am Asking God For: Today I Want To Know:

Today's Compliment To Myself: What Would I Like To Express?

Nightly Thoughts

What Happened Today?   Today I Tried My Best To:

What Did I Like About My Day?   Someone Told Me:

Today I Thought About:

I Am Proud Of Myself For: Tonight's Self-Talk:

Girls Can Do Anything.

What Calms Me Down When I Am Upset?

A Girl's World

Date: Mood:

Morning Thoughts

I Am Grateful For: I Am Excited About:

Today I Am Asking God For: Today I Want To Know:

Today's Compliment To Myself: What Would I Like To Express?

Nightly Thoughts

What Happened Today?   Today I Tried My Best To:

What Did I Like About My Day?   Someone Told Me:

Today I Thought About:

I Am Proud Of Myself For: Tonight's Self-Talk:

A Girl's World

Date: Mood:

Morning Thoughts

I Am Grateful For: I Am Excited About:

Today I Am Asking God For: Today I Want To Know:

Today's Compliment To Myself: What Would I Like To Express?

Nightly Thoughts

What Happened Today?   Today I Tried My Best To:

What Did I Like About My Day?   Someone Told Me:

Today I Thought About:

I Am Proud Of Myself For: Tonight's Self-Talk:

A Girl's World

Date: Mood:

Morning Thoughts

I Am Grateful For:

Today I Am Asking God For:

Today's Compliment To Myself:

I Am Excited About:

Today I Want To Know:

What Would I Like To Express?

Nightly Thoughts

What Happened Today?

What Did I Like About My Day?

Today I Thought About:

I Am Proud Of Myself For:

Today I Tried My Best To:

Someone Told Me:

Tonight's Self-Talk:

I Deserve To Be Spoiled. I Am A Princess!

What Do I Like The Most About Myself?

A Girl's World

Date: Mood:

Morning Thoughts

I Am Grateful For:

Today I Am Asking God For:

Today's Compliment To Myself:

I Am Excited About:

Today I Want To Know:

What Would I Like To Express?

Nightly Thoughts

What Happened Today?

What Did I Like About My Day?

Today I Thought About:

I Am Proud Of Myself For:

Today I Tried My Best To:

Someone Told Me:

Tonight's Self-Talk:

A Girl's World

Date: Mood:

Morning Thoughts

I Am Grateful For: I Am Excited About:

Today I Am Asking God For: Today I Want To Know:

Today's Compliment To Myself: What Would I Like To Express?

Nightly Thoughts

What Happened Today?   Today I Tried My Best To:

What Did I Like About My Day?   Someone Told Me:

Today I Thought About:

I Am Proud Of Myself For: Tonight's Self-Talk:

A Girl's World

Date: Mood:

Morning Thoughts

I Am Grateful For:

Today I Am Asking God For:

Today's Compliment To Myself:

I Am Excited About:

Today I Want To Know:

What Would I Like To Express?

Nightly Thoughts

What Happened Today?

What Did I Like About My Day?

Today I Thought About:

I Am Proud Of Myself For:

Today I Tried My Best To:

Someone Told Me:

Tonight's Self-Talk:

Girl, You Are Just Incredible!

A Girl's World

Date: Mood:

Morning Thoughts

I Am Grateful For: I Am Excited About:

Today I Am Asking God For: Today I Want To Know:

Today's Compliment To Myself: What Would I Like To Express?

Nightly Thoughts

What Happened Today?   Today I Tried My Best To:

What Did I Like About My Day?   Someone Told Me:

Today I Thought About:

I Am Proud Of Myself For: Tonight's Self-Talk:

A Girl's World

Date: Mood:

Morning Thoughts

I Am Grateful For: I Am Excited About:

Today I Am Asking God For: Today I Want To Know:

Today's Compliment To Myself: What Would I Like To Express?

Nightly Thoughts

What Happened Today?   Today I Tried My Best To:

What Did I Like About My Day?   Someone Told Me:

Today I Thought About:

I Am Proud Of Myself For: Tonight's Self-Talk:

I Am

Blessed.

A Girl's World

Date: Mood:

Morning Thoughts

I Am Grateful For: I Am Excited About:

Today I Am Asking God For: Today I Want To Know:

Today's Compliment To Myself: What Would I Like To Express?

Nightly Thoughts

What Happened Today?   Today I Tried My Best To:

What Did I Like About My Day?   Someone Told Me:

Today I Thought About:

I Am Proud Of Myself For: Tonight's Self-Talk:

A Girl's World

Date: Mood:

Morning Thoughts

I Am Grateful For: I Am Excited About:

Today I Am Asking God For: Today I Want To Know:

Today's Compliment To Myself: What Would I Like To Express?

Nightly Thoughts

What Happened Today?   Today I Tried My Best To:

What Did I Like About My Day?   Someone Told Me:

Today I Thought About:

I Am Proud Of Myself For: Tonight's Self-Talk:

A Girl's World

Date: Mood:

Morning Thoughts

I Am Grateful For: I Am Excited About:

Today I Am Asking God For: Today I Want To Know:

Today's Compliment To Myself: What Would I Like To Express?

Nightly Thoughts

What Happened Today?   Today I Tried My Best To:

What Did I Like About My Day?   Someone Told Me:

Today I Thought About:

I Am Proud Of Myself For: Tonight's Self-Talk:

Mr. Kittens

1 - orange   2 - red   3 - green   4 - yellow   5 - brown

6 - pink   7 - blue   8 - light blue   9 - black

I Can Change The World.

A Girl's World

Date: Mood:

Morning Thoughts

I Am Grateful For: I Am Excited About:

Today I Am Asking God For: Today I Want To Know:

Today's Compliment To Myself: What Would I Like To Express?

Nightly Thoughts

What Happened Today?   Today I Tried My Best To:

What Did I Like About My Day?   Someone Told Me:

Today I Thought About:

I Am Proud Of Myself For: Tonight's Self-Talk:

A Girl's World

Date: Mood:

Morning Thoughts

I Am Grateful For:

Today I Am Asking God For:

Today's Compliment To Myself:

I Am Excited About:

Today I Want To Know:

What Would I Like To Express?

Nightly Thoughts

What Happened Today?

What Did I Like About My Day?

Today I Thought About:

I Am Proud Of Myself For:

Today I Tried My Best To:

Someone Told Me:

Tonight's Self-Talk:

A Girl's World

Date: Mood:

Morning Thoughts

I Am Grateful For: I Am Excited About:

Today I Am Asking God For: Today I Want To Know:

Today's Compliment To Myself: What Would I Like To Express?

Nightly Thoughts

What Happened Today?   Today I Tried My Best To:

What Did I Like About My Day?   Someone Told Me:

Today I Thought About:

I Am Proud Of Myself For: Tonight's Self-Talk:

A Girl's World

Date: _____   Mood: _____

Morning Thoughts

I Am Grateful For:

I Am Excited About:

Today I Am Asking God For:

Today I Want To Know:

Today's Compliment To Myself:

What Would I Like To Express?

Nightly Thoughts

What Happened Today?

Today I Tried My Best To:

What Did I Like About My Day?

Someone Told Me:

Today I Thought About:

I Am Proud Of Myself For:

Tonight's Self-Talk:

It Is Okay Not To Be Perfect.

A Girl's World

Date: Mood:

Morning Thoughts

I Am Grateful For: I Am Excited About:

Today I Am Asking God For: Today I Want To Know:

Today's Compliment To Myself: What Would I Like To Express?

Nightly Thoughts

What Happened Today?   Today I Tried My Best To:

What Did I Like About My Day?   Someone Told Me:

Today I Thought About:

I Am Proud Of Myself For: Tonight's Self-Talk:

242

A Girl's World

Date: Mood:

Morning Thoughts

I Am Grateful For: I Am Excited About:

Today I Am Asking God For: Today I Want To Know:

Today's Compliment To Myself: What Would I Like To Express?

Nightly Thoughts

What Happened Today?   Today I Tried My Best To:

What Did I Like About My Day?   Someone Told Me:

Today I Thought About:

I Am Proud Of Myself For: Tonight's Self-Talk:

A Girl's World

Date: _____   Mood: _____

Morning Thoughts

I Am Grateful For:

Today I Am Asking God For:

Today's Compliment To Myself:

I Am Excited About:

Today I Want To Know:

What Would I Like To Express?

Nightly Thoughts

What Happened Today?

What Did I Like About My Day?

Today I Thought About:

I Am Proud Of Myself For:

Today I Tried My Best To:

Someone Told Me:

Tonight's Self-Talk:

If You Don't See Anyone Who Looks Like You Doing Something You Want To Do, Don't Be Afraid To Be The First One To Do It.

A Girl's World

Date: Mood:

Morning Thoughts

I Am Grateful For:

I Am Excited About:

Today I Am Asking God For:

Today I Want To Know:

Today's Compliment To Myself:

What Would I Like To Express?

Nightly Thoughts

What Happened Today?

Today I Tried My Best To:

What Did I Like About My Day?

Someone Told Me:

Today I Thought About:

I Am Proud Of Myself For:

Tonight's Self-Talk:

A Girl's World

Date: Mood:

Morning Thoughts

I Am Grateful For:

I Am Excited About:

Today I Am Asking God For:

Today I Want To Know:

Today's Compliment To Myself:

What Would I Like To Express?

Nightly Thoughts

What Happened Today?

Today I Tried My Best To:

What Did I Like About My Day?

Someone Told Me:

Today I Thought About:

I Am Proud Of Myself For:

Tonight's Self-Talk:

A Girl's World

Date: Mood:

Morning Thoughts

I Am Grateful For: I Am Excited About:

Today I Am Asking God For: Today I Want To Know:

Today's Compliment To Myself: What Would I Like To Express?

Nightly Thoughts

What Happened Today?   Today I Tried My Best To:

What Did I Like About My Day?   Someone Told Me:

Today I Thought About:

I Am Proud Of Myself For: Tonight's Self-Talk:

Who Do I Trust And Why?

I Do Not Have To Have It All Figured Out.

A Girl's World

Date: Mood:

Morning Thoughts

I Am Grateful For: I Am Excited About:

Today I Am Asking God For: Today I Want To Know:

Today's Compliment To Myself: What Would I Like To Express?

Nightly Thoughts

What Happened Today?   Today I Tried My Best To:

What Did I Like About My Day?   Someone Told Me:

Today I Thought About:

I Am Proud Of Myself For: Tonight's Self-Talk:

A Girl's World

Date: Mood:

Morning Thoughts

I Am Grateful For: I Am Excited About:

Today I Am Asking God For: Today I Want To Know:

Today's Compliment To Myself: What Would I Like To Express?

Nightly Thoughts

What Happened Today?   Today I Tried My Best To:

What Did I Like About My Day?   Someone Told Me:

Today I Thought About:

I Am Proud Of Myself For: Tonight's Self-Talk:

A Girl's World

Date: Mood:

Morning Thoughts

I Am Grateful For:

I Am Excited About:

Today I Am Asking God For:

Today I Want To Know:

Today's Compliment To Myself:

What Would I Like To Express?

Nightly Thoughts

What Happened Today?

Today I Tried My Best To:

What Did I Like About My Day?

Someone Told Me:

Today I Thought About:

I Am Proud Of Myself For:

Tonight's Self-Talk:

A Girl's World

Date: Mood:

Morning Thoughts

I Am Grateful For: I Am Excited About:

Today I Am Asking God For: Today I Want To Know:

Today's Compliment To Myself: What Would I Like To Express?

Nightly Thoughts

What Happened Today?   Today I Tried My Best To:

What Did I Like About My Day?   Someone Told Me:

Today I Thought About:

I Am Proud Of Myself For: Tonight's Self-Talk:

She is more
precious than
rubies;
nothing you
desire can compare
with her.

-proverbs 3:15

A Girl's World

Date: Mood:

Morning Thoughts

I Am Grateful For: I Am Excited About:

Today I Am Asking God For: Today I Want To Know:

Today's Compliment To Myself: What Would I Like To Express?

Nightly Thoughts

What Happened Today?   Today I Tried My Best To:

What Did I Like About My Day?   Someone Told Me:

Today I Thought About:

I Am Proud Of Myself For: Tonight's Self-Talk:

A Girl's World

Date: Mood:

Morning Thoughts

I Am Grateful For:

I Am Excited About:

Today I Am Asking God For:

Today I Want To Know:

Today's Compliment To Myself:

What Would I Like To Express?

Nightly Thoughts

What Happened Today?

Today I Tried My Best To:

What Did I Like About My Day?

Someone Told Me:

Today I Thought About:

I Am Proud Of Myself For:

Tonight's Self-Talk:

A Girl's World

Date: Mood:

Morning Thoughts

I Am Grateful For: I Am Excited About:

Today I Am Asking God For: Today I Want To Know:

Today's Compliment To Myself: What Would I Like To Express?

Nightly Thoughts

What Happened Today?   Today I Tried My Best To:

What Did I Like About My Day?   Someone Told Me:

Today I Thought About:

I Am Proud Of Myself For: Tonight's Self-Talk:

I Show Self-Control By....

She is clothed
with strength and
dignity;
she can laugh
at the days to come.

- Proverbs 31:25

A Girl's World

Date: Mood:

Morning Thoughts

I Am Grateful For: I Am Excited About:

Today I Am Asking God For: Today I Want To Know:

Today's Compliment To Myself: What Would I Like To Express?

Nightly Thoughts

What Happened Today?   Today I Tried My Best To:

What Did I Like About My Day?   Someone Told Me:

Today I Thought About:

I Am Proud Of Myself For: Tonight's Self-Talk:

A Girl's World

Date: Mood:

Morning Thoughts

I Am Grateful For: I Am Excited About:

Today I Am Asking God For: Today I Want To Know:

Today's Compliment To Myself: What Would I Like To Express?

Nightly Thoughts

What Happened Today?   Today I Tried My Best To:

What Did I Like About My Day?   Someone Told Me:

Today I Thought About:

I Am Proud Of Myself For: Tonight's Self-Talk:

A Girl's World

Date: Mood:

Morning Thoughts

I Am Grateful For: I Am Excited About:

Today I Am Asking God For: Today I Want To Know:

Today's Compliment To Myself: What Would I Like To Express?

Nightly Thoughts

What Happened Today?   Today I Tried My Best To:

What Did I Like About My Day?   Someone Told Me:

Today I Thought About:

I Am Proud Of Myself For: Tonight's Self-Talk:

A Girl's World

Date: Mood:

Morning Thoughts

I Am Grateful For:

I Am Excited About:

Today I Am Asking God For:

Today I Want To Know:

Today's Compliment To Myself:

What Would I Like To Express?

Nightly Thoughts

What Happened Today?

Today I Tried My Best To:

What Did I Like About My Day?

Someone Told Me:

Today I Thought About:

I Am Proud Of Myself For:

Tonight's Self-Talk:

I Am Great Too!

Five Things That Make Me Laugh....

1.

2.

3.

4.

5.

A Girl's World

Date: Mood:

Morning Thoughts

I Am Grateful For: I Am Excited About:

Today I Am Asking God For: Today I Want To Know:

Today's Compliment To Myself: What Would I Like To Express?

Nightly Thoughts

What Happened Today?   Today I Tried My Best To:

What Did I Like About My Day?   Someone Told Me:

Today I Thought About:

I Am Proud Of Myself For: Tonight's Self-Talk:

A Girl's World

Date: Mood:

Morning Thoughts

I Am Grateful For: I Am Excited About:

Today I Am Asking God For: Today I Want To Know:

Today's Compliment To Myself: What Would I Like To Express?

Nightly Thoughts

What Happened Today?   Today I Tried My Best To:

What Did I Like About My Day?   Someone Told Me:

Today I Thought About:

I Am Proud Of Myself For: Tonight's Self-Talk:

A Girl's World

Date: Mood:

Morning Thoughts

I Am Grateful For: I Am Excited About:

Today I Am Asking God For: Today I Want To Know:

Today's Compliment To Myself: What Would I Like To Express?

Nightly Thoughts

What Happened Today?   Today I Tried My Best To:

What Did I Like About My Day?   Someone Told Me:

Today I Thought About:

I Am Proud Of Myself For: Tonight's Self-Talk:

A Girl's World

Date: _____   Mood: _____

Morning Thoughts

I Am Grateful For:

I Am Excited About:

Today I Am Asking God For:

Today I Want To Know:

Today's Compliment To Myself:

What Would I Like To Express?

Nightly Thoughts

What Happened Today?

Today I Tried My Best To:

What Did I Like About My Day?

Someone Told Me:

Today I Thought About:

I Am Proud Of Myself For:

Tonight's Self-Talk:

A Girl's World

Date: Mood:

Morning Thoughts

I Am Grateful For: I Am Excited About:

Today I Am Asking God For: Today I Want To Know:

Today's Compliment To Myself: What Would I Like To Express?

Nightly Thoughts

What Happened Today?   Today I Tried My Best To:

What Did I Like About My Day?   Someone Told Me:

Today I Thought About:

I Am Proud Of Myself For: Tonight's Self-Talk:

A Girl's World

Date: Mood:

Morning Thoughts

I Am Grateful For: I Am Excited About:

Today I Am Asking God For: Today I Want To Know:

Today's Compliment To Myself: What Would I Like To Express?

Nightly Thoughts

What Happened Today?   Today I Tried My Best To:

What Did I Like About My Day?   Someone Told Me:

Today I Thought About:

I Am Proud Of Myself For: Tonight's Self-Talk:

A Girl's World

Date: Mood:

Morning Thoughts

I Am Grateful For: I Am Excited About:

Today I Am Asking God For: Today I Want To Know:

Today's Compliment To Myself: What Would I Like To Express?

Nightly Thoughts

What Happened Today?   Today I Tried My Best To:

What Did I Like About My Day?   Someone Told Me:

Today I Thought About:

I Am Proud Of Myself For: Tonight's Self-Talk:

Thank You God.

A Girl's World

Date: Mood:

Morning Thoughts

I Am Grateful For: I Am Excited About:

Today I Am Asking God For: Today I Want To Know:

Today's Compliment To Myself: What Would I Like To Express?

Nightly Thoughts

What Happened Today?   Today I Tried My Best To:

What Did I Like About My Day?   Someone Told Me:

Today I Thought About:

I Am Proud Of Myself For: Tonight's Self-Talk:

A Girl's World

Date: Mood:

Morning Thoughts

I Am Grateful For: I Am Excited About:

Today I Am Asking God For: Today I Want To Know:

Today's Compliment To Myself: What Would I Like To Express?

Nightly Thoughts

What Happened Today?   Today I Tried My Best To:

What Did I Like About My Day?   Someone Told Me:

Today I Thought About:

I Am Proud Of Myself For: Tonight's Self-Talk:

A Girl's World

Date: Mood:

Morning Thoughts

I Am Grateful For: I Am Excited About:

Today I Am Asking God For: Today I Want To Know:

Today's Compliment To Myself: What Would I Like To Express?

Nightly Thoughts

What Happened Today?   Today I Tried My Best To:

What Did I Like About My Day?   Someone Told Me:

Today I Thought About:

I Am Proud Of Myself For: Tonight's Self-Talk:

A Girl's World

Date: Mood:

Morning Thoughts

I Am Grateful For: I Am Excited About:

Today I Am Asking God For: Today I Want To Know:

Today's Compliment To Myself: What Would I Like To Express?

Nightly Thoughts

What Happened Today?   Today I Tried My Best To:

What Did I Like About My Day?   Someone Told Me:

Today I Thought About:

I Am Proud Of Myself For: Tonight's Self-Talk:

I Am

```
Q W N O J C R B C K T O J K Y U Y U
F E E T U O E X E P O S I T I V E C
D S W O R T H Y V A S P S F Z G U P
M R W S K D G J X E U W V Y Q J B Q
I N T E N T I O N A L T J W F F A L
T C M D E M Z I I L F G I B J A F U
H P R V G T P S M N C F J F C B V H
W S G E R P S H S B G F G V U U I A
Z U A C A E X C E P T I O N A L N I
F T Z H C T X C V M Q D I U G O T D
G R V N E X I Q M Q L E F R S U E D
B V I O F E V V N O L T E X L S L K
E R T F U N L J E T B C Z Y V B L A
P D F B L O V I N G E O M W Z C I H
T A I N T E R E S T I N G A Y L G I
U F M Z I F G L A M O R O U S K E T
X A G K D F R I E N D L Y S T I N A
U K Z T J C O M P A S S I O N A T E
```

Beautiful
Compassionate
Creative
Exceptional
Fabulous
Friendly
Fun
Gentle
Glamorous
Graceful

Happiness
Intelligent
Intentional
Interesting
Loving
Outgoing
Positive
Princess
Sweet
Worthy

Completed Word Search Can Be Found On Page 331

A Girl's World

Date: Mood:

Morning Thoughts

I Am Grateful For:

Today I Am Asking God For:

Today's Compliment To Myself:

I Am Excited About:

Today I Want To Know:

What Would I Like To Express?

Nightly Thoughts

What Happened Today?

What Did I Like About My Day?

Today I Thought About:

I Am Proud Of Myself For:

Today I Tried My Best To:

Someone Told Me:

Tonight's Self-Talk:

A Girl's World

Date: Mood:

Morning Thoughts

I Am Grateful For: I Am Excited About:

Today I Am Asking God For: Today I Want To Know:

Today's Compliment To Myself: What Would I Like To Express?

Nightly Thoughts

What Happened Today?   Today I Tried My Best To:

What Did I Like About My Day?   Someone Told Me:

Today I Thought About:

I Am Proud Of Myself For: Tonight's Self-Talk:

A Girl's World

Date: Mood:

Morning Thoughts

I Am Grateful For: I Am Excited About:

Today I Am Asking God For: Today I Want To Know:

Today's Compliment To Myself: What Would I Like To Express?

Nightly Thoughts

What Happened Today?   Today I Tried My Best To:

What Did I Like About My Day?   Someone Told Me:

Today I Thought About:

I Am Proud Of Myself For: Tonight's Self-Talk:

Seven Fun Facts About Me....

1.

2.

3.

4.

5.

6.

7.

There Is Nothing Wrong With Me.

A Girl's World

Date: Mood:

Morning Thoughts

I Am Grateful For: I Am Excited About:

Today I Am Asking God For: Today I Want To Know:

Today's Compliment To Myself: What Would I Like To Express?

Nightly Thoughts

What Happened Today?   Today I Tried My Best To:

What Did I Like About My Day?   Someone Told Me:

Today I Thought About:

I Am Proud Of Myself For: Tonight's Self-Talk:

A Girl's World

Date: Mood:

Morning Thoughts

I Am Grateful For: I Am Excited About:

Today I Am Asking God For: Today I Want To Know:

Today's Compliment To Myself: What Would I Like To Express?

Nightly Thoughts

What Happened Today?   Today I Tried My Best To:

What Did I Like About My Day?   Someone Told Me:

Today I Thought About:

I Am Proud Of Myself For: Tonight's Self-Talk:

A Girl's World

Date: Mood:

Morning Thoughts

I Am Grateful For: I Am Excited About:

Today I Am Asking God For: Today I Want To Know:

Today's Compliment To Myself: What Would I Like To Express?

Nightly Thoughts

What Happened Today?   Today I Tried My Best To:

What Did I Like About My Day?   Someone Told Me:

Today I Thought About:

I Am Proud Of Myself For: Tonight's Self-Talk:

A Girl's World

Date: Mood:

Morning Thoughts

I Am Grateful For:

I Am Excited About:

Today I Am Asking God For:

Today I Want To Know:

Today's Compliment To Myself:

What Would I Like To Express?

Nightly Thoughts

What Happened Today?

Today I Tried My Best To:

What Did I Like About My Day?

Someone Told Me:

Today I Thought About:

I Am Proud Of Myself For:

Tonight's Self-Talk:

A Girl's World

Date: Mood:

Morning Thoughts

I Am Grateful For: I Am Excited About:

Today I Am Asking God For: Today I Want To Know:

Today's Compliment To Myself: What Would I Like To Express?

Nightly Thoughts

What Happened Today?   Today I Tried My Best To:

What Did I Like About My Day?   Someone Told Me:

Today I Thought About:

I Am Proud Of Myself For: Tonight's Self-Talk:

A Girl's World

Date: Mood:

Morning Thoughts

I Am Grateful For: I Am Excited About:

Today I Am Asking God For: Today I Want To Know:

Today's Compliment To Myself: What Would I Like To Express?

Nightly Thoughts

What Happened Today?   Today I Tried My Best To:

What Did I Like About My Day?   Someone Told Me:

Today I Thought About:

I Am Proud Of Myself For: Tonight's Self-Talk:

A Girl's World

Date: Mood:

Morning Thoughts

I Am Grateful For: I Am Excited About:

Today I Am Asking God For: Today I Want To Know:

Today's Compliment To Myself: What Would I Like To Express?

Nightly Thoughts

What Happened Today?   Today I Tried My Best To:

What Did I Like About My Day?   Someone Told Me:

Today I Thought About:

I Am Proud Of Myself For: Tonight's Self-Talk:

A Girl's World

Date: Mood:

Morning Thoughts

I Am Grateful For: I Am Excited About:

Today I Am Asking God For: Today I Want To Know:

Today's Compliment To Myself: What Would I Like To Express?

Nightly Thoughts

What Happened Today?   Today I Tried My Best To:

What Did I Like About My Day?   Someone Told Me:

Today I Thought About:

I Am Proud Of Myself For: Tonight's Self-Talk:

A Girl's World

Date: Mood:

Morning Thoughts

I Am Grateful For: I Am Excited About:

Today I Am Asking God For: Today I Want To Know:

Today's Compliment To Myself: What Would I Like To Express?

Nightly Thoughts

What Happened Today?   Today I Tried My Best To:

What Did I Like About My Day?   Someone Told Me:

Today I Thought About:

I Am Proud Of Myself For: Tonight's Self-Talk:

A Girl's World

Date: Mood:

Morning Thoughts

I Am Grateful For: I Am Excited About:

Today I Am Asking God For: Today I Want To Know:

Today's Compliment To Myself: What Would I Like To Express?

Nightly Thoughts

What Happened Today?   Today I Tried My Best To:

What Did I Like About My Day?   Someone Told Me:

Today I Thought About:

I Am Proud Of Myself For: Tonight's Self-Talk:

A Girl's World

Date: Mood:

Morning Thoughts

I Am Grateful For: I Am Excited About:

Today I Am Asking God For: Today I Want To Know:

Today's Compliment To Myself: What Would I Like To Express?

Nightly Thoughts

What Happened Today?   Today I Tried My Best To:

What Did I Like About My Day?   Someone Told Me:

Today I Thought About:

I Am Proud Of Myself For: Tonight's Self-Talk:

A Girl's World

Date: Mood:

Morning Thoughts

I Am Grateful For:

I Am Excited About:

Today I Am Asking God For:

Today I Want To Know:

Today's Compliment To Myself:

What Would I Like To Express?

Nightly Thoughts

What Happened Today?

Today I Tried My Best To:

What Did I Like About My Day?

Someone Told Me:

Today I Thought About:

I Am Proud Of Myself For:

Tonight's Self-Talk:

What Has Been My Best Year So Far And Why?

A Girl's World

Date: Mood:

Morning Thoughts

I Am Grateful For: I Am Excited About:

Today I Am Asking God For: Today I Want To Know:

Today's Compliment To Myself: What Would I Like To Express?

Nightly Thoughts

What Happened Today?   Today I Tried My Best To:

What Did I Like About My Day?   Someone Told Me:

Today I Thought About:

I Am Proud Of Myself For: Tonight's Self-Talk:

A Girl's World

Date: _____   Mood: _____

Morning Thoughts

I Am Grateful For:

I Am Excited About:

Today I Am Asking God For:

Today I Want To Know:

Today's Compliment To Myself:

What Would I Like To Express?

Nightly Thoughts

What Happened Today?

Today I Tried My Best To:

What Did I Like About My Day?

Someone Told Me:

Today I Thought About:

I Am Proud Of Myself For:

Tonight's Self-Talk:

A Girl's World

Date: Mood:

Morning Thoughts

I Am Grateful For: I Am Excited About:

Today I Am Asking God For: Today I Want To Know:

Today's Compliment To Myself: What Would I Like To Express?

Nightly Thoughts

What Happened Today?   Today I Tried My Best To:

What Did I Like About My Day?   Someone Told Me:

Today I Thought About:

I Am Proud Of Myself For: Tonight's Self-Talk:

Being The Center Of Attention Feels....

A Girl's World

Date: Mood:

Morning Thoughts

I Am Grateful For: I Am Excited About:

Today I Am Asking God For: Today I Want To Know:

Today's Compliment To Myself: What Would I Like To Express?

Nightly Thoughts

What Happened Today?   Today I Tried My Best To:

What Did I Like About My Day?   Someone Told Me:

Today I Thought About:

I Am Proud Of Myself For: Tonight's Self-Talk:

A Girl's World

Date: Mood:

Morning Thoughts

I Am Grateful For:

Today I Am Asking God For:

Today's Compliment To Myself:

I Am Excited About:

Today I Want To Know:

What Would I Like To Express?

Nightly Thoughts

What Happened Today?

What Did I Like About My Day?

Today I Thought About:

I Am Proud Of Myself For:

Today I Tried My Best To:

Someone Told Me:

Tonight's Self-Talk:

A Girl's World

Date: Mood:

Morning Thoughts

I Am Grateful For:

I Am Excited About:

Today I Am Asking God For:

Today I Want To Know:

Today's Compliment To Myself:

What Would I Like To Express?

Nightly Thoughts

What Happened Today?

Today I Tried My Best To:

What Did I Like About My Day?

Someone Told Me:

Today I Thought About:

I Am Proud Of Myself For:

Tonight's Self-Talk:

God is within her, she will not fall; God will help her at break of day.

- Psalm 46:5

If I Could Talk To Any Celebrity Who Would I Talk To, What Would I Ask Them And What Would We Talk About?

A Girl's World

Date: Mood:

Morning Thoughts

I Am Grateful For:

I Am Excited About:

Today I Am Asking God For:

Today I Want To Know:

Today's Compliment To Myself:

What Would I Like To Express?

Nightly Thoughts

What Happened Today?

Today I Tried My Best To:

What Did I Like About My Day?

Someone Told Me:

Today I Thought About:

I Am Proud Of Myself For:

Tonight's Self-Talk:

A Girl's World

Date: Mood:

Morning Thoughts

I Am Grateful For: I Am Excited About:

Today I Am Asking God For: Today I Want To Know:

Today's Compliment To Myself: What Would I Like To Express?

Nightly Thoughts

What Happened Today?   Today I Tried My Best To:

What Did I Like About My Day?   Someone Told Me:

Today I Thought About:

I Am Proud Of Myself For: Tonight's Self-Talk:

A Girl's World

Date: Mood:

Morning Thoughts

I Am Grateful For: I Am Excited About:

Today I Am Asking God For: Today I Want To Know:

Today's Compliment To Myself: What Would I Like To Express?

Nightly Thoughts

What Happened Today?   Today I Tried My Best To:

What Did I Like About My Day?   Someone Told Me:

Today I Thought About:

I Am Proud Of Myself For: Tonight's Self-Talk:

The Traveling Turtle

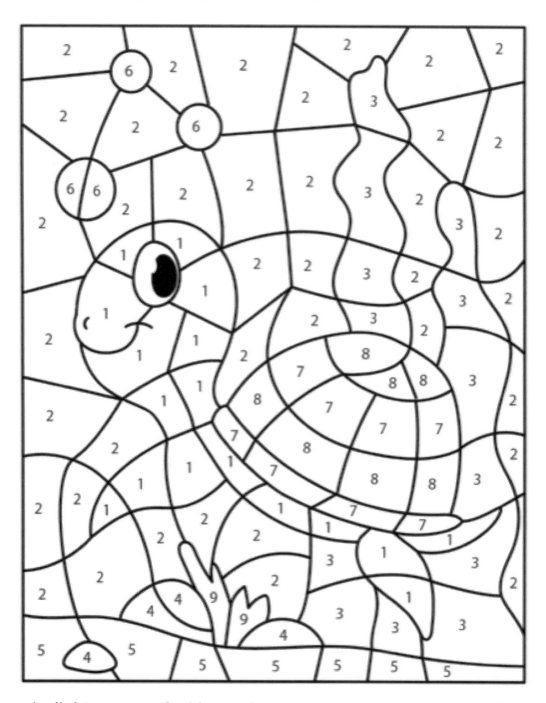

1 - light green   2 - blue   3 - green   4 - brown   5 - yellow

6 - light blue   7 - orange   8 - red   9 - dark green

If I Was Given $5,000, How Would I Spend It?

A Girl's World

Date: Mood:

Morning Thoughts

I Am Grateful For: I Am Excited About:

Today I Am Asking God For: Today I Want To Know:

Today's Compliment To Myself: What Would I Like To Express?

Nightly Thoughts

What Happened Today?   Today I Tried My Best To:

What Did I Like About My Day?   Someone Told Me:

Today I Thought About:

I Am Proud Of Myself For: Tonight's Self-Talk:

A Girl's World

Date: Mood:

Morning Thoughts

I Am Grateful For: I Am Excited About:

Today I Am Asking God For: Today I Want To Know:

Today's Compliment To Myself: What Would I Like To Express?

Nightly Thoughts

What Happened Today?   Today I Tried My Best To:

What Did I Like About My Day?   Someone Told Me:

Today I Thought About:

I Am Proud Of Myself For: Tonight's Self-Talk:

A Girl's World

Date: Mood:

Morning Thoughts

I Am Grateful For: I Am Excited About:

Today I Am Asking God For: Today I Want To Know:

Today's Compliment To Myself: What Would I Like To Express?

Nightly Thoughts

What Happened Today?   Today I Tried My Best To:

What Did I Like About My Day?   Someone Told Me:

Today I Thought About:

I Am Proud Of Myself For: Tonight's Self-Talk:

A Girl's World

Date: Mood:

Morning Thoughts

I Am Grateful For: I Am Excited About:

Today I Am Asking God For: Today I Want To Know:

Today's Compliment To Myself: What Would I Like To Express?

Nightly Thoughts

What Happened Today?   Today I Tried My Best To:

What Did I Like About My Day?   Someone Told Me:

Today I Thought About:

I Am Proud Of Myself For: Tonight's Self-Talk:

A Girl's World

Date: Mood:

Morning Thoughts

I Am Grateful For: I Am Excited About:

Today I Am Asking God For: Today I Want To Know:

Today's Compliment To Myself: What Would I Like To Express?

Nightly Thoughts

What Happened Today?   Today I Tried My Best To:

What Did I Like About My Day?   Someone Told Me:

Today I Thought About:

I Am Proud Of Myself For: Tonight's Self-Talk:

A Girl's World

Date: Mood:

Morning Thoughts

I Am Grateful For: I Am Excited About:

Today I Am Asking God For: Today I Want To Know:

Today's Compliment To Myself: What Would I Like To Express?

Nightly Thoughts

What Happened Today?   Today I Tried My Best To:

What Did I Like About My Day?   Someone Told Me:

Today I Thought About:

I Am Proud Of Myself For: Tonight's Self-Talk:

A Girl's World

Date: Mood:

Morning Thoughts

I Am Grateful For: I Am Excited About:

Today I Am Asking God For: Today I Want To Know:

Today's Compliment To Myself: What Would I Like To Express?

Nightly Thoughts

What Happened Today?   Today I Tried My Best To:

What Did I Like About My Day?   Someone Told Me:

Today I Thought About:

I Am Proud Of Myself For: Tonight's Self-Talk:

When I Do Not Know Something, I Simply Ask.

A Girl's World

Date: Mood:

Morning Thoughts

I Am Grateful For: I Am Excited About:

Today I Am Asking God For: Today I Want To Know:

Today's Compliment To Myself: What Would I Like To Express?

Nightly Thoughts

What Happened Today?   Today I Tried My Best To:

What Did I Like About My Day?   Someone Told Me:

Today I Thought About:

I Am Proud Of Myself For: Tonight's Self-Talk:

A Girl's World

Date: Mood:

Morning Thoughts

I Am Grateful For: I Am Excited About:

Today I Am Asking God For: Today I Want To Know:

Today's Compliment To Myself: What Would I Like To Express?

Nightly Thoughts

What Happened Today?   Today I Tried My Best To:

What Did I Like About My Day?   Someone Told Me:

Today I Thought About:

I Am Proud Of Myself For: Tonight's Self-Talk:

A Girl's World

Date: _____   Mood: _____

Morning Thoughts

I Am Grateful For:

Today I Am Asking God For:

Today's Compliment To Myself:

I Am Excited About:

Today I Want To Know:

What Would I Like To Express?

Nightly Thoughts

What Happened Today?

What Did I Like About My Day?

Today I Thought About:

I Am Proud Of Myself For:

Today I Tried My Best To:

Someone Told Me:

Tonight's Self-Talk:

A Girl's World

Date: Mood:

Morning Thoughts

I Am Grateful For: I Am Excited About:

Today I Am Asking God For: Today I Want To Know:

Today's Compliment To Myself: What Would I Like To Express?

Nightly Thoughts

What Happened Today?   Today I Tried My Best To:

What Did I Like About My Day?   Someone Told Me:

Today I Thought About:

I Am Proud Of Myself For: Tonight's Self-Talk:

A Girl's World

Date: Mood:

Morning Thoughts

I Am Grateful For: I Am Excited About:

Today I Am Asking God For: Today I Want To Know:

Today's Compliment To Myself: What Would I Like To Express?

Nightly Thoughts

What Happened Today?   Today I Tried My Best To:

What Did I Like About My Day?   Someone Told Me:

Today I Thought About:

I Am Proud Of Myself For: Tonight's Self-Talk:

A Girl's World

Date: Mood:

Morning Thoughts

I Am Grateful For: I Am Excited About:

Today I Am Asking God For: Today I Want To Know:

Today's Compliment To Myself: What Would I Like To Express?

Nightly Thoughts

What Happened Today?   Today I Tried My Best To:

What Did I Like About My Day?   Someone Told Me:

Today I Thought About:

I Am Proud Of Myself For: Tonight's Self-Talk:

Completed

Word

Searches

I Feel

```
P  H  W  N  A  P  Q  O  L  C  S  H  K  W  K  P  V  C
B  B  U  N  O  E  Q  V  O  J  I  R  S  N  Y  Z  W  W
B  B  N  N  W  I  I  P  V  G  X  A  T  N  H  Z  D  E
D  E  P  N  Q  A  B  C  A  G  R  Q  H  W  E  O  U
I  N  Z  J  O  H  C  P  B  E  T  L  X  I  T  H  P  C
W  A  R  N  K  T  J  C  L  J  G  A  Y  A  H  V  F  B
K  T  R  D  S  G  N  Y  E  L  W  O  V  A  W  B  S  T
V  Q  P  U  G  G  I  E  A  P  Z  I  W  E  T  J  P  A
T  Y  S  B  E  R  E  X  W  I  T  C  O  F  R  W  T  N
H  O  G  C  R  G  L  U  D  O  K  E  N  N  C  T  B  U
O  W  V  U  B  D  A  Y  M  N  C  R  D  S  T  L  E  B
R  H  H  L  X  F  T  C  M  J  N  N  E  X  X  U  D  B
E  U  O  N  J  T  V  C  R  J  H  A  R  E  L  Y  M  Z
Q  C  T  F  E  U  H  E  P  M  J  M  F  H  O  G  C  T
Y  P  N  R  Y  X  R  R  V  F  Q  C  U  Q  E  X  B  K
A  N  P  H  V  B  Y  H  X  Q  Z  A  L  Z  J  U  D  S
E  H  G  V  K  N  C  Z  K  X  Z  E  E  O  K  P  I  B
G  B  Y  H  S  Z  I  Q  I  Y  Q  S  L  K  M  Z  L  X
```

Accepted	Pretty
Lovable	Wonderful
Motivated	

Nature

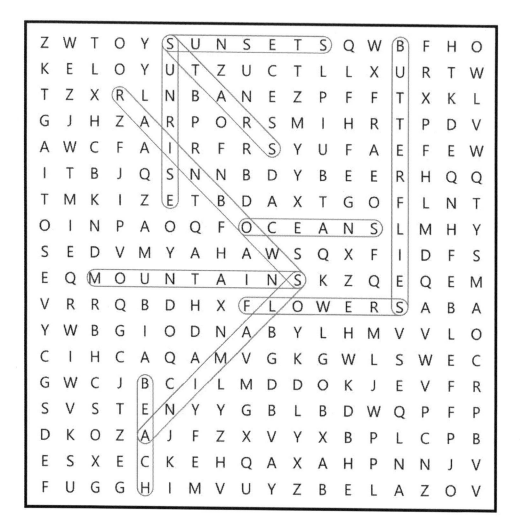

Z W T O Y S U N S E T S Q W B F H O
K E L O Y U T Z U C T L L X U R T W
T Z X R L N B A N E Z P F F T X K L
G J H Z A R P O R S M I H R T P D V
A W C F A I R F R S Y U F A E F E W
I T B J Q S N N B D Y B E E R H Q Q
T M K I Z E T B D A X T G O F L N T
O I N P A O Q F O C E A N S L M H Y
S E D V M Y A H A W S Q X F I D F S
E Q M O U N T A I N S K Z Q E Q E M
V R R Q B D H X F L O W E R S A B A
Y W B G I O D N A B Y L H M V V L O
C I H C A Q A M V G K G W L S W E C
G W C J B C I L M D D O K J E V F R
S V S T E N Y Y G B L B D W Q P F P
D K O Z A J F Z X V Y X B P L C P B
E S X E C K E H Q A X A H P N N J V
F U G G H I M V U Y Z B E L A Z O V

Animals	Oceans
Beach	Rainbows
Butterflies	Stars
Flowers	Sunrise
Mountains	Sunsets

Random Fun Things To Do

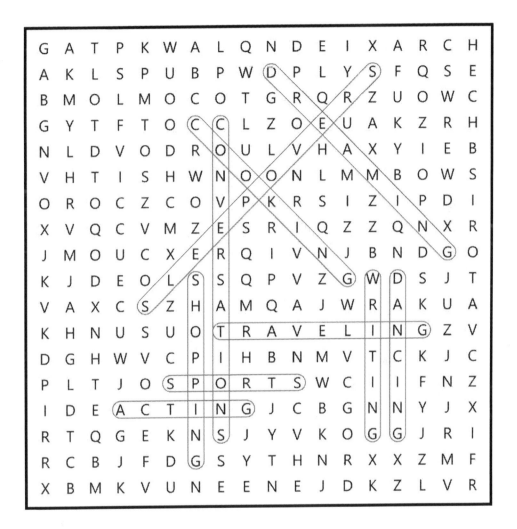

Acting

Conversations

Cooking

Dancing

Dreaming

Shopping

Sleepovers

Sports

Traveling

Writing

God Is

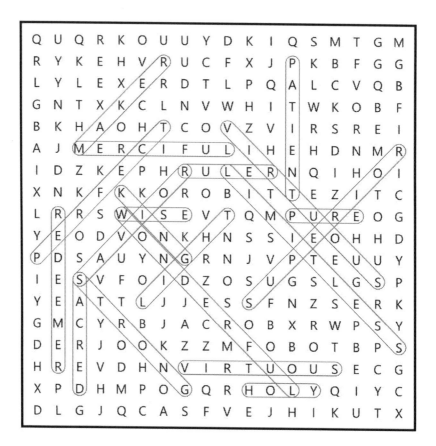

Holy	Ruler
King	Sacred
Light	Savior
Limitless	Strong
Maker	Superior
Merciful	Virtuous
Patient	Virtuous
Perfect	Wise
Pure	Wonderful
Redeemer	

I Am

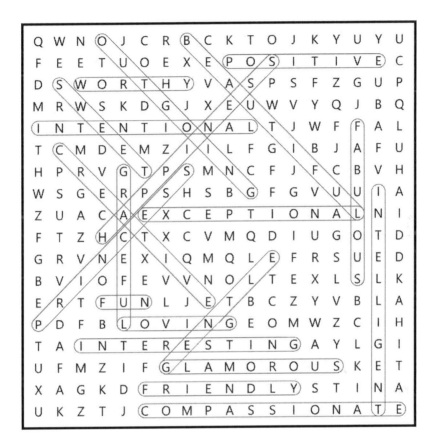

Beautiful
Compassionate
Creative
Exceptional
Fabulous
Friendly
Fun
Gentle
Glamorous
Graceful

Happiness
Intelligent
Intentional
Interesting
Loving
Outgoing
Positive
Princess
Sweet
Worthy

Made in the USA
Middletown, DE
16 September 2022